ALICE IN WONDERLAND PUZZLES

with original illustrations by Sir John Tenniel

Dr Gareth Moore

This edition published in 2020 by Arcturus Publishing Limited
26/27 Bickels Yard, 151–153 Bermondsey Street,
London SE1 3HA

AD008551UK

Printed in the UK

Contents ❧

Introduction ✇

Lewis Carroll, the author of both *Alice's Adventures in Wonderland* and its sequel, *Through the Looking-Glass, and What Alice Found There* was a huge fan of puzzles. He created many of his own, and is often said to have invented the word ladder, a popular puzzle. He also created various cryptographic ciphers, allowing messages to be hidden in plain sight by encoding the letters in cunning ways.

Even Lewis Carroll's writing name was a puzzle. His real name was in fact Charles Lutwidge Dodgson, but he created his pen name by first translating his given names into Latin, resulting in Carolus Ludovicus. This he then translated back into English, resulting in Carol Lewis. Finally, he reversed those names to end up with his famous alter ego: Lewis Carroll.

This book is packed full of all kinds of puzzles. Some are types that Charles Dodgson would have been familiar with, such as rebus puzzles or word ladders, of course. However, many are far more modern inventions that will be new even to most contemporary readers. There is also a wide range of lateral-thinking puzzles, where you will need to use your skill and intuition to puzzle out the most likely solution to a given conundrum. Still further puzzles require you to think logically or to use your word skills. And occasionally, and only when explicitly stated, some puzzles will rely on your knowledge of the original stories.

Once you're ready to begin your journey into Wonderland, why not turn the page and accompany Alice on her latest puzzling adventures?

All excerpts are from *Alice's Adventures in Wonderland* and *Through the Looking-Glass, and What Alice Found There* by Lewis Carroll.

Time for Wonderland

One fine day, Alice was lying on the riverbank, idly picking daisies with the intention of chaining them together, when she heard a small, squeaky, and rather panicked voice.

"Oh dear!" it said. "I'm going to be late!"

Alice turned to find the source of the voice, hoping to perhaps offer some words of assurance. To her great surprise it was coming from a White Rabbit, who was hurrying past her and checking his pocket watch with what seemed to Alice to be an unnecessary frequency.

"Excuse me," she said, not altogether sure of the proper way to address a rabbit with a pocket watch.

"What is it?" the Rabbit answered irritably. "Can't you see I'm in a rush?"

"I'm sorry," replied Alice. "But I just wondered whether I might be able to help you."

The Rabbit's frown softened, or so she fancied, but it was hard to tell on a creature without eyebrows.

"As a matter of fact, you could," he replied. "Can you tell me the time? My pocket watch takes on five minutes for every hour, and I haven't reset it since 8 p.m. yesterday evening."

Alice didn't have a pocket watch of her own, but she thought she might be able to help the rabbit anyway.

"What time does your pocket watch say it is now?" she asked.

"Twelve twenty-eight," the rabbit told her.

What time did that mean it really was?

Can you answer
Alice's question?

Down the Rabbit Hole ❧

After Alice had helped the White Rabbit to ascertain the correct time, he immediately hurried off, still lamenting loudly.

"I'm going to be late! Oh, I'm going to be much too late!"

Her curiosity piqued, Alice decided to follow after the Rabbit, determined to discover where it was that a White Rabbit with a pocket watch might be trying to get to in such a hurry. She caught up with him just in time to see him disappearing into a large rabbit hole. With only a moment's hesitation, Alice went in after him.

She found herself in a maze-like warren of tunnels, with earth crumbling all around her. The Rabbit clearly knew these tunnels well, for he darted through them so quickly that he was soon out of sight.

Can you help Alice find her way through the maze of tunnels, from the top to the bottom? You'll notice that some of the tunnels have small bridges that you can walk under or where you can cross through to other tunnels, making it much more confusing than it would otherwise be.

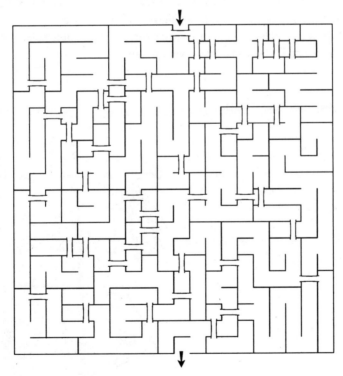

The Long Fall

Alice emerged from the maze of tunnels and, before she knew it, she noticed that she was falling into what seemed to be a very deep well. She fell and she fell and she fell, and still there was no sign of the bottom of the well. She felt strangely calm, even though she had been falling for such a long time. It didn't seem as if she was going very fast, and she thought that perhaps it wouldn't be too painful if she did eventually reach the bottom, so long as there was something soft there to break her fall: soft pillows, perhaps, or a nice pile of leaves.

After all, thought Alice, her father had once been working on the house and had fallen clean off a twenty-foot ladder. There had been nothing to break his fall, and yet he had not been hurt at all.

What mundane explanation is there for how Alice's father had survived his fall without injury?

The Shrinking Bottle ❧

Alice eventually floated gently down to the ground, and found herself in a room without any visible exit. There was, however, a single bottle sitting right in the middle of a single table. The bottle had a label on it: DRINK ME.

Never one to lack curiosity, Alice immediately opened the bottle and smelled its contents. It didn't *smell* like it was dangerous, so she took a cautious sip. All at once, Alice had the strangest sensation. She felt she was shrinking, and indeed the ground *did* seem to be getting closer. After a moment or two, much to Alice's interest, this stopped, and when she looked around she observed that she had shrunk to two-thirds of her usual height. Intrigued, she took a second sip, and again she began to shrink, this time shrinking to two-thirds of the height she had just been.

From this new perspective, Alice was able to see a very small door at the bottom of the wall. It couldn't have been more than 5 cm high and this, she decided, must be the way out.

Given that Alice was 120 cm tall before she began to drink from the bottle, how many more sips did she need to take before she would be able to walk normally through the door without bending over?

Tweedledum and Tweedledee 1 ✑

Alice left the room and immediately came upon the White Rabbit, who welcomed her to Wonderland and gave her what he evidently considered sage advice but which seemed to Alice to be nothing but a stream of nonsense. He then scurried off behind a bush, thus vanishing from Alice's view.

Alice was minded to follow, when two identical men dressed in identical caps and identical dungarees suddenly came into view and addressed her directly.

"Hello, young lady," said the one on the left.

"And who might you be?" said the one on the right.

"For I'm Tweedledum," said the one on the left.

"And I'm Tweedledee," said the one on the right.

Alice was suddenly grateful to the White Rabbit, for he had mentioned these two. He had warned her of their mischievousness, and warned her that at least one of them always lied.

Given this information, what was the name of the man of on the left?

"Tweedledum and Tweedledee"

Excerpt from *Through the Looking-Glass, and What Alice Found There*, chapter IV

"If you think we're wax-works," he said, "you ought to pay, you know. Wax-works weren't made to be looked at for nothing. Nohow!"

"Contrariwise," added the one marked "DEE," "if you think we're alive, you ought to speak."

"I'm sure I'm very sorry," was all Alice could say; for the words of the old song kept ringing through her head like the ticking of a clock, and she could hardly help saying them out loud:—

> *"Tweedledum and Tweedledee*
> *Agreed to have a battle;*
> *For Tweedledum said Tweedledee*
> *Had spoiled his nice new rattle.*
>
> *Just then flew down a monstrous crow,*
> *As black as a tar-barrel;*
> *Which frightened both the heroes so,*
> *They quite forgot their quarrel."*

"I know what you're thinking about," said Tweedledum: "but it isn't so, nohow."

"Contrariwise," continued Tweedledee, "if it was so, it might be; and if it were so, it would be; but as it isn't, it ain't. That's logic."

Too Big for Court ☙

Lots of things in Wonderland made Alice change size, but perhaps the biggest she grew was when she was at court as a witness for the trial of the Knave of Hearts. On that occasion they had tried to banish her from court for violating Rule 42: *No persons more than a mile tall are allowed in court.* But in fact, Alice wasn't quite a mile high. Rather, she was 40 feet tall plus a third of her actual height.

How tall was she?

Remembering Forward

One of the strangest characters Alice came across during her travels in Wonderland was the White Queen. She lived through a looking glass, so she lived partially backward in time. This meant that she felt the effects of things before they happened, and could remember things from the future.

"Sometimes I wish I could predict the future," Alice said to her, when she found out about this strange power.

"Well, of course you can, dear," said the White Queen. "It's quite simple."

What did she mean? How could Alice predict the future without use of any magical powers?

Not Enough Tea ❧

At a party one day, the Mad Hatter laid out nine tea cups in a surprisingly neat row. He began to pour steaming pink tea into them from an absurdly ornate and long-spouted teapot. As he filled the fourth cup, however, the stream of tea reduced to a dribble, and it became clear that the pot was empty.

"The tea's run out," said the March Hare.

"It's stopped running out," said the Hatter.

"I think he means there isn't any left," said Alice.

"Yes there is," said the Hatter. "It's in the cups."

"But there isn't enough for the rest of the cups," Alice said.

"True," said the Hatter. "It's lucky there are only three of us."

A miserable squeak came from the teapot.

"Four of us," the March Hare corrected.

"True," said the Hatter. "Now here's a challenge for you, Alice. At the moment, all four filled teacups are at one end of the row, with five empty ones next to them. Can you make them alternate between filled and not filled. But here's the catch: You can move only two of the cups."

How could it be done?

Not Enough Cake

Alice once again came across the White Rabbit, who was looking very upset.

"My dear rabbit! Whatever is wrong?" she asked.

"Why, but I have just been to the Mad Hatter's Tea Party," he sniffled. "They had an enormous carrot cake, which is the kind I like the most. But the Hatter himself took half the slices plus two more, and then the March Hare took half the remaining slices plus two more, and then the Dormouse took half the remaining slices plus two more, and then there wasn't any left for me!"

If this was so, how many slices of cake were there to start with?

Three Bottles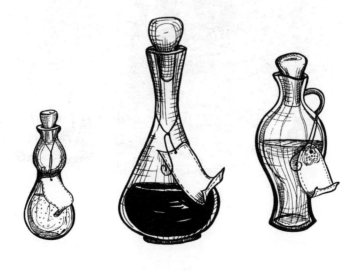

One day, the residents of Wonderland presented Alice with three potion bottles of three different sizes. One was made by the Caterpillar and contained mushroom potion. One was made by the White Rabbit and contained carrot potion. One was made by the Cook and contained pepper potion.

Alice was told that one of the potions would make her shrink, one would make her grow, and one would have no effect on her size. She was also told the following:

- She would end up bigger if she drank from the carrot potion than she would if she drank from the biggest bottle.
- She would end up smaller if she drank from the smallest bottle than she would if she drank from the pepper potion.
- The White Rabbit's potion was not in the smallest bottle.

Based on this information, can you deduce which potion was in which bottle, and how each potion would affect Alice's size?

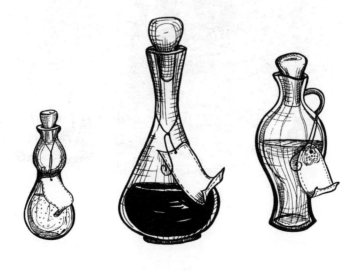

In The Kitchen ⤷

One day Alice found herself in the Duchess's kitchen, helping the Cook to prepare a meal. On a high shelf there was a basket marked POTATOES, a basket marked CARROTS, and a basket marked POTATOES AND CARROTS.

"The Duchess's baby changed the labels," the Cook warned her, "and now they're all wrong. Could you pass me five carrots?"

Alice could only just reach into the baskets, and they were far too heavy to move. What is the fewest number of vegetables Alice needs to reach for in order to work out which basket is which?

The Right Size

Alice came across a door with two locks that were very far apart. She calculated that in order to be able to reach both at the same time, she would need to be exactly 19 cm taller than she currently was. Moreover, she had a potion that made her shrink with each sip, and a cake that made her grow with each bite. The potion made her shrink by 3 cm, and the cake made her grow by 8 cm.

What was the minimum total number of sips and bites she needed to consume in order to reach her precise desired height?

"A Caucus-Race and a Long Tale"

Excerpt from *Alice's Adventures in Wonderland*, chapter III

"What *is* a Caucus-race?" said Alice; not that she wanted much to know, but the Dodo had paused as if it thought that *somebody* ought to speak, and no one else seemed inclined to say anything.

"Why," said the Dodo, "the best way to explain it is to do it." (And, as you might like to try the thing yourself, some winter day, I will tell you how the Dodo managed it.)

First it marked out a race-course, in a sort of circle, ("the exact shape doesn't matter," it said,) and then all the party were placed along the course, here and there. There was no "One, two, three, and away," but they began running when they liked, and left off when they liked, so that it was not easy to know when the race was over. However, when they had been running half an hour or so, and were quite dry again, the Dodo suddenly called out "The race is over!" and they all crowded round it, panting, and asking, "But who has won?"

This question the Dodo could not answer without a great deal of thought, and it sat for a long time with one finger pressed upon its forehead (the position in which you usually see Shakespeare, in the pictures of him), while the rest waited in silence. At last the Dodo said, "*Everybody* has won, and all must have prizes."

"But who is to give the prizes?" quite a chorus of voices asked.

"Why, *she*, of course," said the Dodo, pointing to Alice with one finger; and the whole party at once crowded round her, calling out in a confused way, "Prizes! Prizes!"

Alice had no idea what to do, and in despair she put her hand in her pocket, and pulled out a box of comfits, (luckily the salt water had not got into it), and handed them round as prizes. There was exactly one a-piece all round.

"But she must have a prize herself, you know," said the Mouse.

"Of course," the Dodo replied very gravely. "What else have you got in your pocket?" he went on, turning to Alice.

"Only a thimble," said Alice sadly.

"Hand it over here," said the Dodo.

Then they all crowded round her once more, while the Dodo solemnly presented the thimble, saying "We beg your acceptance of this elegant thimble"; and, when it had finished this short speech, they all cheered.

The Head Start

The Mad Hatter and the March Hare decided to have a race. They carefully measured out a course of 100 m, using hats to mark the start and finish. They had Alice stand at the finish line in case it was a close call. But, as it turned out, the March Hare won the race by 10 m.

"I want a rematch!" said the Hatter to the Hare. "And as you're faster, you should start further back!"

The Hare agreed that this seemed fair. Since he had won by 10 m, they started him 10 m before the original start line.

Assuming both the Hatter and the Hare ran at the same speed they had in the previous race, who would win in this new arrangement?

In this Style 10/6

The Not Lemonade

Alice was helping the Cook in the Duchess's kitchen. It was a hot day, so when they had finished cooking the Cook poured them some lemonade on ice. The Duchess drank hers almost immediately, but the slightly peppery taste made Alice rather struggle with hers, particularly because she kept sneezing between every sip.

She eventually managed to finish the whole glass, but as she made to stand up she discovered she had shrunk down to the size of a large cat. The Cook, however, had been completely unaffected by her drink.

Given that they were drinking the same thing, and both would react to Wonderland magic in the same way, can you find something that could explain why Alice shrank but the cook did not?

Cake Selection 🥢

"What types of cake do you have?" Alice asked the Mad Hatter one day.

"Well, that is an easy question, with an easy answer: All but two of them are carrot cakes, all but two of them are jam sponges, and all but two of them are coffee cakes," he told her.

How many cakes did the Mad Hatter have in total?

The Sentence

"Off with his head!" said the Red Queen, when the Knave of Hearts was found guilty of a crime. But the Knave pleaded for a different sentence, and so the Queen came up with some alternatives.

She said, "Your choices are as follows: you may be beheaded, set on fire, or locked in a room with a Bandersnatch that hasn't eaten in two months."

What should the Knave have chosen?

Tweedledum and Tweedledee 2 ✎

After their first run-in, when both Tweedledum and Tweedledee had lied to Alice about their names, she had managed to convince Tweedledum of the value of honesty, and persuaded him to start telling the truth. Tweedledee, however, remained resolute in his resolve to lie about everything. The trouble was that with the two brothers being so very identical, Alice could never tell which of them was which, and as a result she never knew whether the brother she was addressing was speaking truthfully or not.

"Are you Tweedledum?" she asked one of them, upon coming across them in a clearing.

"If I am Tweedledum," he said, "then my brother is Tweedledee."

Did this answer help Alice to determine which brother she was speaking to?

"Pig & Pepper"

Excerpt from *Alice's Adventures in Wonderland,*
chapter IV

"What sort of people live about here?"

"In *that* direction," the Cat said, waving its right paw round, "lives a Hatter: and in *that* direction," waving the other paw, "lives a March Hare. Visit either you like: they're both mad."

"But I don't want to go among mad people," Alice remarked.

"Oh, you can't help that," said the Cat: "we're all mad here. I'm mad. You're mad."

"How do you know I'm mad?" said Alice.

"You must be," said the Cat, "or you wouldn't have come here."

Alice didn't think that proved it at all; however, she went on: "And how do you know that you're mad?"

"To begin with," said the Cat, "a dog's not mad. You grant that?"

"I suppose so," said Alice.

"Well, then," the Cat went on, "you see, a dog growls when it's angry, and wags its tail when it's pleased. Now *I* growl when I'm pleased, and wag my tail when I'm angry. Therefore I'm mad."

Too Many Queens

"Have you seen the White Queen?" Alice asked the Cheshire Cat.

"Queens," said the Cheshire Cat. "They move very fast on a chessboard, you know."

"They move along rows, columns, or diagonals, and can move any number of squares" said Alice. "I know."

"But here's an interesting question. How many queens could you place on an 8×8 chessboard without any of them being able to attack another on their first move?"

Shifting Words 1 ～

The Mad Hatter has shifted the letters of the following Lewis Carroll quotation five places forward alphabetically.

Can you shift them back to reveal the question?

Bmd nx f wfajs qnpj f bwnynsl-ijxp?

Tea Party Invitations ❧

"I'm inviting people for tea," said the Mad Hatter. "Alice, would you give out these invitations?"

Alice looked at the names on the envelopes. "I don't understand," she said. "Who are all these people?"

"Oh yes, I haven't written their names in the usual way," he explained. "I think letters must get so tired of being in the same order all the time, so I've jumbled them up. I'm sure you can work them out though, my dear."

Alice looked at the envelopes again. The names were as follows:
- Hectic Share
- A Frequent Shoe
- Bib With Tear
- Freaks Have Not
- Mutter Lock

Can you unscramble the names and work out who the Mad Hatter had invited?

Down the Stairs

There was a single staircase in the Duchess's house. When Alice went inside and began to grow, she was able to climb the steps of the staircase five steps at a time, leaving her with three steps to hop up at the top. Once she had shrunk back down she could only jump down three steps at a time, leaving her with two steps to hop down right at the bottom.

What is the smallest number of steps there could have been in the staircase?

Magic Mushrooms

The Caterpillar gave Alice three baskets, each of which contained two mushrooms. One basket was marked Two for Growing, one was marked Two for Shrinking, and the third was marked One for Growing and One for Shrinking.

"Of course," the Caterpillar told her, "it would be dreadfully dull if the baskets were correctly marked. Thus I have mixed up the labels so that each basket has the wrong label."

Alice would not have been opposed to the dreadfully dull state of affairs in which all baskets were correctly marked, but she decided not to argue. Instead, she thanked the Caterpillar and headed on her way. As she walked, she found herself beginning to shrink. The more she shrank, the slower she became, and she decided that it was worth trying to eat one of the mushrooms the Caterpillar had given her in the hope that it might reverse her shrinking.

From which basket should she take a mushroom to maximize her chances of getting a growing mushroom?

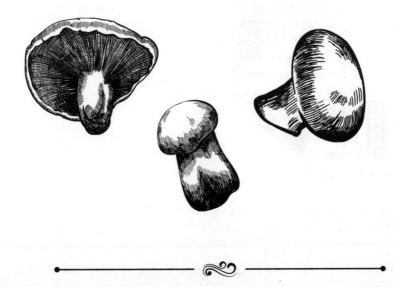

A Pie Problem

Alice was packing away pies in the Duchess's kitchen. The Cook had given Alice sixteen pies and four boxes of different sizes in which to pack them.

"I want four pies in each box," she told Alice. "No more and no less."

Alice had set out the four boxes on the table, and had just managed to squeeze four pies into each box when the White Rabbit came charging into the kitchen.

"Have you seen the Duchess's gloves?" he asked. "Oh dear, oh dear, I'm going to be late, and I can't find the gloves!"

As he did a frantic circuit of the kitchen, he collided with the table, knocking two boxes of pies onto the floor. Alice retrieved the boxes, but to her dismay the pies inside had broken and she had to throw them away.

"Look what you've done!" she said to the rabbit, which only made him more distressed. "Now I can't put four pies into each box!"

"Oh dear, oh dear," he said, throwing her a concerned look, and then hurried away.

Alice sat down and looked at the boxes of pies and felt tears starting in her eyes. She didn't want to make the Cook angry again, but she didn't see what she could do. Then, however, a solution occurred to her.

How was Alice able to pack the eight remaining pies so that each of the four boxes contained exactly four pies?

The Hand that was Dealt ✎

The Mad Hatter, the March Hare, and the Dormouse were each holding a single playing card. One of these cards was a two, one was a seven, and one was a queen. One was a club, one was a diamond, and one was a heart.

Alice also knew the following:
- The Hare's card was higher than the diamond.
- The seven's suit was earlier in the alphabet than the Dormouse's suit.
- The queen was not the queen of hearts.

Can you deduce which card each of the three held?

Shifting Words 2 🐛

The Mad Hatter has shifted backward the letters of the following Lewis Carroll quotation by a certain number of places alphabetically. Can you work out the shift and reveal the quotation?

**Gr bmcql'r kyrrcp ufgaf uyw wms em...
Qm jmle yq G ecr qmkcufcpc.**

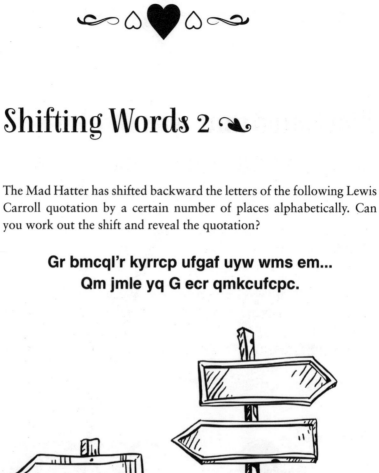

Tweedledum and Tweedledee 3 🐌

The next time Alice came across Tweedledum and Tweedledee, they were talking to a little dormouse.

"I'd never steal a piece of cheese," said the Dormouse. "So let me go now, if you please!"

"Does he lie or tell the truth?" Alice asked the brothers.

"He always lies," said one of the brothers.

"He sometimes lies," said the other brother.

So does the Dormouse lie, tell the truth, or both?

"The Rabbit Sends in a Little Bill"

Excerpt from *Alice's Adventures in Wonderland,* chapter IV

Alice looked all round her at the flowers and the blades of grass, but she could not see anything that looked like the right thing to eat or drink under the circumstances. There was a large mushroom growing near her, about the same height as herself; and when she had looked under it, and on both sides of it, and behind it, it occurred to her that she might as well look and see what was on the top of it.

She stretched herself up on tiptoe, and peeped over the edge of the mushroom, and her eyes immediately met those of a large blue caterpillar, that was sitting on the top with its arms folded, quietly smoking a long hookah, and taking not the smallest notice of her or of anything else.

Strange Sequences 1 ∾

While sitting atop his mushroom and smoking merrily, the Caterpillar's latest habit is to pose passers-by a continue-the-sequence question. By way of incentive to partake in his game, he gives a piece of a magical mushroom to the passer-by who is able to provide the correct next letter.

Can you identify which letter should come next in the following timely sequence?

YYHLYEY _

The Three Pieces ❧

Alice was once told about three chess pieces on a board: a bishop, a pawn, and a rook. Numbering the chess board columns from A to H, and the rows from 1 to 8, one piece was in column A, one in column B, and one in column E. One piece was in row 3, one in row 4, and one in row 7.

Alice also knew the following:
- The pawn was in a higher row number than the piece in column B.
- The piece in row four was in an earlier column letter than the bishop.
- The piece in row 4 moved three times as many squares in its previous turn as the piece in column A.

Can you deduce which piece was in which square of the board?

Looking Through the Looking Glass ❧

One day, before making her way through the looking glass, Alice had peered into it and was surprised to see a collection of books on a shelf with their names written in a strange tongue. She guessed that it must be the language of Wonderland. Among the titles she saw were:

- *Dribgnik Comal Likot*, by Eel Reprah
- *Eyreh Tnireh Ctaceht*, by Regnilas Dj
- *Ekaws Nagen Nif*, by Ecyoj Semaj
- *Dnalred Nowni Serutnev Dasecila*, by Llorrac Siwel

Can you translate these titles into English?

Strange Sequences 2 ❧

Still sitting atop his mushroom and smoking merrily, the Caterpillar continues his habit of posing passers-by a continue-the-sequence question. By way of incentive to partake in his game, he gives a piece of a magical mushroom to the passer-by who is able to provide the correct next letter.

Can you identify which letter should come next in the following sequence?

W T F S S M _

Shifting Words 3 ✒

The Mad Hatter has shifted forward the letters of the following Lewis Carroll quotation by a certain number of places alphabetically. Can you deduce the shift and identify the quotation?

Ib tmiab Q svwe epw Q eia epmv Q owb cx bpqa uwzvqvo, jcb Q bpqvs Q ucab pidm jmmv kpivoml amdmzit bquma aqvkm bpmv.

Hidden Figures

A Wonderland character is hiding within each of these sentences. Can you find them all?

- It was during the original ice age.

- Taekwondo doesn't require much equipment.

- I made an angry phone call.

- The plan for renewal rushed us.

- I found that terrifying.

Character Match-up

Can you match up the words in the left and right columns to make the names of eight Wonderland residents?

CHESHIRE	BIRD
HUMPTY	CAT
FROG	DUMPTY
JUBJUB	FOOTMAN
MAD	HARE
MARCH	HATTER
MOCK	KING
RED	RABBIT
WHITE	TURTLE

Too Many Legs

When Alice first arrived in Wonderland, she came across a large group of animals. Most of them were birds of different sorts, and the rest were mice. The birds all had two legs, as birds so often do, and the mice all had four, again the most common arrangement.

Alice counted that all together the birds and mice had 26 heads and 64 legs.

Can you work out how many birds and how many mice there were?

"Who Stole the Tarts?"
Excerpt from *Alice's Adventures in Wonderland,* chapter XI

The King and Queen of Hearts were seated on their throne when they arrived, with a great crowd assembled about them—all sorts of little birds and beasts, as well as the whole pack of cards: the Knave was standing before them, in chains, with a soldier on each side to guard him; and near the King was the White Rabbit, with a trumpet in one hand, and a scroll of parchment in the other. In the very middle of the court was a table, with a large dish of tarts upon it: they looked so good, that it made Alice quite hungry to look at them—"I wish they'd get the trial done," she thought, "and hand round the refreshments!" But there seemed to be no chance of this, so she began looking at everything about her, to pass away the time.

"Herald, read the accusation!" said the King.

On this the White Rabbit blew three blasts on the trumpet, and then unrolled the parchment scroll, and read as follows:

"The Queen of Hearts, she made some tarts,
  All on a summer day:
The Knave of Hearts, he stole those tarts,
  And took them quite away!"

"Consider your verdict," the King said to the jury.

Stolen Vowels 1

The Knave of Hearts has stolen all of the vowels and spaces from these Wonderland residents.

Can you restore them all?

CTRPLLR

DRMS

MDHTTR

RDKNG

WHTRBBT

Strange Sequences 3 ❧

Still sitting atop his mushroom and smoking merrily, the Caterpillar continues his habit of posing passers-by a continue-the-sequence question. By way of incentive to partake in his game, he gives a piece of a magical mushroom to the passer-by who is able to provide the correct next letter.

Can you identify which letter should come next in the following sequence of last letters?

D E W N E O _

Strange Sequences 4 &

The Caterpillar then sets a teaser which he is sure will prove a challenge to even the most intelligent of passers-by.

Can you solve it by identifying which letter should come next in the following sequence?

H H L B B C N O _

Stolen Vowels 2

The Knave of Hearts has stolen all of the vowels and spaces from these Wonderland residents.

Can you restore them all?

BNDRSNTCH

CHSHRCT

MCKTRTL

MRCHHR

TWDLDM

Split Titles 1 🌿

The titles of six chapters of *Alice's Adventures in Wonderland* have each been split into two groups of alternating letters. Can you reunite each group from the left with its pair on the right?

A_A_T_A_A_T_   _D_I_E_R_M_C_T_R_I_L_R

A_V_C_F_O_A_A_E_P_L_A_   _H_M_C_T_R_L_S_T_R_

L_B_T_R_U_D_I_L_   _H_Q_E_N_C_O_U_T_R_U_D

T_E_A_B_T_E_D_A_I_T_E_I_L   _H_R_B_I_S_N_S_L_T_L_B_L_

T_E_O_K_U_T_E_S_O_Y   _M_D_E_P_R_Y

T_E_U_E_S_R_Q_E_G_O_N_   _O_S_E_Q_A_R_L_E

Wonderful Words

Can you join these words into pairs with a Carrollian theme?
One word is the odd one out, since it pairs with itself.

- A
- Ah
- Arts
- Cater
- Corn
- Do
- Foot
- He
- Hook
- Land
- Lice
- Man
- Mush
- Pillar
- Room
- Wonder
- Uni

Split Titles 2 ❧

The titles of six chapters of *Alice's Adventures in Wonderland* have each been split into two groups of alternating letters. Can you reunite each group from the left with its pair on the right?

A_I_E_E_I_E_C_   _H_C_U_U_R_C_A_D_L_N_T_L_

D_W_T_E_A_B_T_O_E   _H_P_O_O_T_A_S

P_G_N_P_P_E_   _I_A_D_E_P_R

T_E_A_C_S_A_E_N_A_O_G_A_E   _H_S_O_E_H_T_R_S

T_E_O_L_F_E_R_   _L_C_S_V_D_N_E

W_O_T_L_T_E_A_T_   _O_N_H_R_B_I_H_L_

Strange Sequences 5

Still sitting atop his mushroom and smoking merrily, the Caterpillar continues his habit of posing passers-by a continue-the-sequence question. By way of incentive to partake in his game, he gives a piece of a magical mushroom to the passer-by who is able to provide the correct next letter.

Can you identify which letter should come next in the following secondary ordering?

OTTFFSS _

Tweedledum
and Tweedledee 4 ~

On one occasion, Alice brought Tweedledum and Tweedledee to the Mad Hatter's tea party. There was a great selection of food, including three types of cake: chocolate cakes, jam sponges, and currant cakes. The brothers set about eating as many of these little cakes as they could.

"Which of the cakes is the nicest?" Alice asked them.

"Either the chocolate cakes are not the worst, or the jam sponges are the best," said one brother.

"The chocolate cakes are not the worst," said the other brother.

Assuming the two brothers agreed on how nice the cakes were, can you use their statements to rank the cakes from best to worst?

An Abundance of Tea ❧

The Mad Hatter's table was overcrowded with teacups. He explained to Alice that a month ago he had decided that, starting with one cup on the first day, he was going to pour one more cup of tea every day than he had the previous day.

On which day of this exercise did the Hatter pour his 150th cup of tea?

"A Caucus-Race and a Long Tale"

Excerpt from *Alice's Adventures in Wonderland,* chapter III

"You promised to tell me your history, you know," said Alice, "and why it is you hate—C and D," she added in a whisper, half afraid that it would be offended again.

"Mine is a long and a sad tale!" said the Mouse, turning to Alice, and sighing.

"It *is* a long tail, certainly," said Alice, looking down with wonder at the Mouse's tail; "but why do you call it sad?" And she kept on puzzling about it while the Mouse was speaking, so that her idea of the tale was something like this:—

"Fury said to a
mouse, That he
met in the
house,
'Let us
both go to
law: *I* will
prosecute
you.– Come,
I'll take no
denial; We
must have a
trial: For
really this
morning I've
nothing
to do.'
Said the
mouse to the
cur, 'Such
a trial
dear Sir,
With
no jury
or judge,
would be
wasting
our
breath.'
'I'll be
judge, I'll
be jury,'
said
cunning
old Fury:
'I'll
try the
whole
cause,
and
condemn
you
to
death.'"

In Other Words

Can you identify these Wonderland characters from synonyms of their names?

- The loopy milliner

- The parade leveret

- The ridicule reptile

- The feline um column

Changing Sizes ❧

This morning, afternoon, and evening, Alice has been three different heights: 50 cm tall, 150 cm tall, and 300 cm tall. One of these heights was caused by her eating a mushroom, one by her eating a cake, and one by her drinking a potion.

Alice remembers the following:
- Eating the mushroom made her taller than she was during the afternoon.
- She ate the cake before she consumed whatever made her 150 cm tall.
- The cake made her grow.

Can you deduce what she consumed at which time of day, and how tall it made her?

The Wrong Names

The Duchess was having a party. There were fifteen guests, none of whom Alice had met before. She asked the Duchess's Cook what their names were, and the Cook gave her a list of fifteen names but did not tell her which name belonged to whom. Not wanting her lists of names to go to waste, Alice decided to randomly assign each name to a guest, and used these names to address them. Over the course of the party. only one guest complained about her using the wrong name, although she didn't get to talk to everyone.

"How good my guessing was!" she thought afterward. "To have only upset one person! I wonder if I guessed all the other names correctly?"

What was the probability that Alice had guessed exactly fourteen of the names correctly?

Birds of a Feather

Alice awoke from a dream to find herself surrounded by a large circle of birds. She recognized the Dodo, the Lory, and the Eaglet, but there were many more that she'd never seen before. Starting from the Dodo, she counted the birds in the circle, noting that the 11th bird was directly opposite the 24th bird.

Assuming the birds were evenly spaced around the circle, how many birds were there in total?

A Sponge Shared ❧

Tweedledum and Tweedledee together eat a sponge cake made by the Duchess's Cook. It takes them 20 minutes. If Tweedledum had eaten the cake on his own, it would have taken him 30 minutes.

Assuming each brother has a constant rate of eating, how long would it have taken Tweedledee to eat the cake on his own?

Madness and Nonsense

"Everyone here is at least a little bit mad," said the Cheshire Cat.

"Is madness something you can have different amounts of?" asked Alice. "I thought you either were mad or you weren't."

"Don't be ridiculous," said the Cheshire Cat. "There are all kinds of madness. Why, 70 percent of people in Wonderland are less mad than average."

"That's nonsense," said Alice. "Averages don't work that way!"

Was it nonsense, or could the Cheshire Cat be right?

Shifting Words 4 ❧

The Mad Hatter has shifted backward the letters of the following Lewis Carroll quotation by a certain number of places alphabetically. Can you identify the shift and reveal the quotation?

**Lwn, hdbtixbth X'kt qtaxtkts ph bpcn ph hxm
xbedhhxqat iwxcvh qtudgt qgtpzuphi.**

"Pig & Pepper"

Excerpt from *Alice's Adventures in Wonderland*, chapter IV

Alice went timidly up to the door, and knocked.

"There's no sort of use in knocking," said the Footman, "and that for two reasons. First, because I'm on the same side of the door as you are; secondly, because they're making such a noise inside, no one could possibly hear you." And certainly there was a most extraordinary noise going on within—a constant howling and sneezing, and every now and then a great crash, as if a dish or kettle had been broken to pieces.

"Please, then," said Alice, "how am I to get in?"

"There might be some sense in your knocking," the Footman went on without attending to her, "if we had the door between us. For instance, if you were *inside*, you might knock, and I could let you out, you know." He was looking up into the sky all the time he was speaking, and this Alice thought decidedly uncivil. "But perhaps he can't help it," she said to herself; "his eyes are so *very* nearly at the top of his head. But at any rate he might answer questions.—How am I to get in?" she repeated, aloud.

"I shall sit here," the Footman remarked, "till tomorrow—"

At this moment the door of the house opened, and a large plate came skimming out, straight at the Footman's head: it just grazed his nose, and broke to pieces against one of the trees behind him.

"—or next day, maybe," the Footman continued in the same tone, exactly as if nothing had happened.

"How am I to get in?" asked Alice again, in a louder tone.

"*Are* you to get in at all?" said the Footman. "That's the first question, you know."

It was, no doubt: only Alice did not like to be told so. "It's really dreadful," she muttered to herself, "the way all the creatures argue. It's enough to drive one crazy!"

The Footman seemed to think this a good opportunity for repeating his remark, with variations. "I shall sit here," he said, "on and off, for days and days."

"But what am *I* to do?" said Alice.

"Anything you like," said the Footman, and began whistling.

"Oh, there's no use in talking to him," said Alice desperately: "he's perfectly idiotic!" And she opened the door and went in.

The door led right into a large kitchen, which was full of smoke from one end to the other: the Duchess was sitting on a three-legged stool in the middle, nursing a baby; the cook was leaning over the fire, stirring a large cauldron which seemed to be full of soup.

Too Big for the Kitchen

Alice must have eaten something strange in the Duchess's kitchen, because she was soon growing and growing. In fact, she was doubling in size every minute. By 12:15 she had filled half the kitchen!

At what time would she fill the whole kitchen?

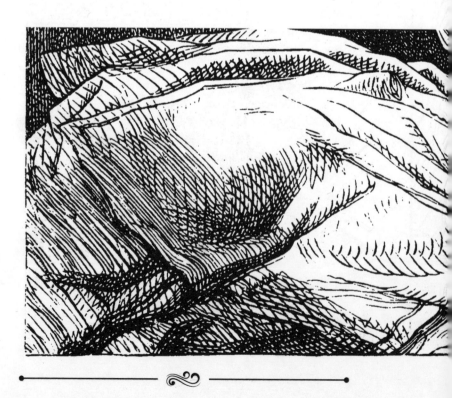

Before the Trial

The trial of the Knave of Hearts was a very hectic affair. Before it began, everyone, from the witnesses to the spectators to the accused, shook hands with everyone else exactly once. Alice calculated that this meant there were 78 handshakes in total.

How many people were at the trial?

Collecting Mushrooms ✘

The Caterpillar had asked Alice to pick 60 mushrooms by dinnertime. She worked out that if she picked mushrooms at a rate of 10 mushrooms an hour, she would manage it just in time. But it turned out to be more difficult than she expected, and she managed to collect the first half of the mushrooms at a rate of only 5 mushrooms an hour.

If she upped her rate to 15 mushrooms an hour for the remaining mushrooms, would she still manage to collect all 60 in time?

Tweedledum and Tweedledee 5 ❧

Alice was on her way to the Royal Garden, where she had been summoned to play croquet with the Queen. While she was following the directions she had been given, she arrived at a fork in the road. She couldn't remember if she was meant to go left or right, or if she'd even been told about the fork at all. She thought and she thought, but nothing came to her, so she sat down where she was and soon felt herself on the verge of tears.

"Is it losing your way that's made you frown?" said a voice.

"Or did you need some sitting down?" said another.

Alice looked up to discover that Tweedledum and Tweedledee were approaching her from the left-hand path in front of her.

"Oh!" she said. "Maybe you can help me! Is that the way to the Royal Garden?"

"It is," replied one of the brothers.

"It isn't," said the other.

"Oh, this is useless," said Alice. "If I don't know which of you is which, you can't help me at all!"

But then she thought of a way to ask her question which would get her the right answer, regardless of whether she was talking to Tweedledum or Tweedledee.

What was it?

Plates of Cakes

The Mad Hatter was distributing cakes onto plates around the table. He put one on the first plate, and then on each subsequent plate he put more cakes than he had on the previous one. Once he'd gone all the way around the table, he'd put down 80 cakes in total.

What is the maximum number of plates there could have been around the table?

Talking Flowers

When Alice first went through the looking-glass, she happened across a vase of flowers that could talk. She was startled at first, but she was quite used to strange things happening, and it soon seemed perfectly natural to her that flowers should talk, and perfectly odd that she'd never heard them talking before.

There were three flowers that she spoke to the most: a rose, a daisy, and a tiger-lily. One of them was white, one was pink, and the third red. Alice also observed that:

- The tiger-lily was taller than the white flower.
- The flower of medium height had a shorter name than the pink flower.
- The pink flower was not the tallest.

Can you deduce which flower was pink, which was red, and which was white, and how tall they were in relation to one another?

Sense and Nonsense

The first sentence of *Alice's Adventures in Wonderland* has been manipulated by altering the vowels. Can you work out how it has been altered, and reveal the original opening sentence?

Eloci wes bigonnong tu git viry torid uf sottong by hir sostir un thi benk, end uf hevong nothong tu du.

Something Forgotten

Alice was wandering around in the woods, with the vague sense that she had forgotten something very important, except that she really couldn't think what it was. She shortly came upon a Fawn with big gentle eyes, who did not look at all troubled to see her.

"Excuse me," she said, "but I wonder if you could help me. You see, I think I've forgotten something, but I'm not sure what it is."

"You have," said the Fawn. "You've forgotten something that belongs to you."

Alice pondered for a moment whether she could have forgotten something that *didn't* belong to her, and she supposed that she could have.

"The curious thing," said the Fawn, "is that although what you've forgotten belongs to you, you don't use it all that much. In fact, other people use it a lot more than you do."

What had Alice forgotten?

Nonsensical Numbers

"Everyone here speaks nonsense," said Alice, with exasperation.

"That's nonsense," said Tweedledum.

"Just because you don't understand it, that doesn't mean it's nonsense," said Tweedledee.

Alice didn't like being accused of not understanding things. "Are you telling me that someone could say 'ten plus seven equals five' and not be speaking nonsense?"

"Sometimes ten plus seven does equal five," said Tweedledum.

"It all depends on what you are doing," said Tweedledee.

So, when does ten plus seven equal five?

"The Walrus and the Carpenter": Part One

Excerpt from *Through the Looking-Glass, and
What Alice Found There*, chapter IV

"The sun was shining on the sea,
        Shining with all his might:
He did his very best to make
        The billows smooth and bright—
And this was odd, because it was
        The middle of the night.

The moon was shining sulkily,
        Because she thought the sun
Had got no business to be there
        After the day was done—
'It's very rude of him,' she said,
        'To come and spoil the fun!'

The sea was wet as wet could be,
        The sands were dry as dry.
You could not see a cloud, because
        No cloud was in the sky:
No birds were flying overhead—
        There were no birds to fly.

The Walrus and the Carpenter
        Were walking close at hand;
They wept like anything to see
        Such quantities of sand:
'If this were only cleared away,'
        They said, 'it would be grand!'

'If seven maids with seven mops
       Swept it for half a year,
Do you suppose,' the Walrus said,
       'That they could get it clear?'
'I doubt it,' said the Carpenter,
       And shed a bitter tear.

'O Oysters, come and walk with us!'
       The Walrus did beseech.
'A pleasant walk, a pleasant talk,
       Along the briny beach:
We cannot do with more than four,
       To give a hand to each.'

POEM CONTINUES ON PAGE 138

Too Many Bishops

Throughout her travels in Wonderland, Alice met many chess pieces, but she never did meet a bishop. She remarked on this to Tweedledum and Tweedledee.

"Yes, well they move in diagonals," said Tweedledum, "so it's easy to miss them."

"Not to mention, they're very antisocial," said Tweedledee.

"Here's a question," said Tweedledum. "How many bishops could you place on a chessboard, so that none of them shared a diagonal, and none of them were in adjacent squares?"

The Dinner Conundrum

One day, Alice was invited to tea, and there were nameplates to show clearly in which place each person was to sit. However, the names had been written in somewhat whimsical ways.

One of the nameplates read:

A. Nits

Who was intended to sit at this seat?

More Sense and Nonsense ❧

The first sentence of *Through the Looking-Glass* has been encoded by altering every other letter. Can you work out how it has been altered, and reveal the original opening sentence?

Ome shhnf wzs beqtzim, tgas tge vhhtd khtsem hzd gac nntgimg so co vish ht—ht var tge alzcj khtsem's eatls emthrdlx.

Tweedledum and Tweedledee 6 ❧

Alice came upon a great river, and was looking for a way to cross it. She saw a small, wooden rowing boat tied to a tree a little way downstream from her and went over to it, planning to untie it and use it to cross the river.

"Excuse me," said a voice, as she was fumbling with the rope, "but that's my boat!"

She turned to discover that either Tweedledum or Tweedledee was standing behind her, and looking rather cross.

That might be Tweedledee instead of Tweedledum, she thought to herself, in which case it's not his boat at all. But I suppose I can't be sure, and either way, he looks as if he'd be angry if I took it.

"May I borrow it?" she asked, hoping his answer might give her a clue as to which of the brothers he was.

"You may borrow it if and only if my name is Tweedledum," he replied.

So should Alice continue trying to untie the boat?

Mathematical Mushroom 1

Can you fill the boxes in this mathematical mushroom with numbers from the range 1 to 9? Each connected number adds together to make the total given at the end of that line, and no number can be repeated within a line.

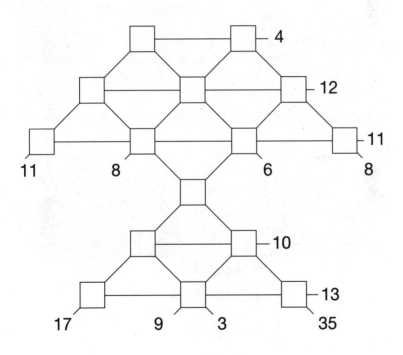

Back to Square One ❧

"How many squares are there on a chessboard?" asked the Red Queen. "That's easy," said Alice, who had learned how to work this kind of thing out at school. "There are eight rows and eight columns, and eight times eight is sixty-four."

"There are sixty-four squares that are one square big, yes, but what about all the larger squares?"

"Larger squares?" asked Alice, perplexed.

"Yes," said the Red Queen. "Squares made up of four little squares, or nine little squares, or sixteen little squares, and so on."

"Oh, I see," said Alice. But even though she understood the question, she had no idea how to go about answering it.

What is the answer?

Broken Chessboard

This chessboard is broken! Can you fit the pieces back together to make an 8×8 chessboard, in which the squares alternate between black and white? The pieces are in the correct orientation, so they don't need to be rotated.

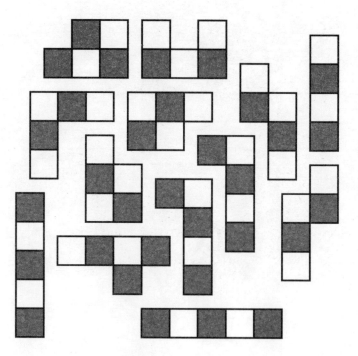

"Looking-Glass House"

Excerpt from *Through the Looking-Glass, and What Alice Found There*, chapter I

"Kitty, can you play chess? Now, don't smile, my dear, I'm asking it seriously. Because, when we were playing just now, you watched just as if you understood it: and when I said 'Check!' you purred! Well, it *was* a nice check, Kitty, and really I might have won, if it hadn't been for that nasty Knight, that came wriggling down among my pieces. Kitty, dear, let's pretend—" And here I wish I could tell you half the things Alice used to say, beginning with her favourite phrase "Let's pretend." She had had quite a long argument with her sister only the day before—all because Alice had begun with "Let's pretend we're kings and queens;" and her sister, who liked being very exact, had argued that they couldn't, because there were only two of them, and Alice had been reduced at last to say, "Well, *you* can be one of them, then, and *I'll* be all the rest." And once she had really frightened her old nurse by shouting suddenly in her ear, "Nurse! Do let's pretend that I'm a hungry hyæna, and you're a bone!"

But this is taking us away from Alice's speech to the kitten. "Let's pretend that you're the Red Queen, Kitty! Do you know, I think if you sat up and folded your arms, you'd look exactly like her. Now do try, there's a dear!"

And Alice got the Red Queen off the table, and set it up before the kitten as a model for it to imitate: however, the thing didn't succeed, principally, Alice said, because the kitten wouldn't fold its arms properly. So, to punish it, she held it up to the Looking-glass, that it might see how sulky it was—"and if you're not good directly," she added, "I'll put you through into Looking-glass House. How would you like *that*?

"Now, if you'll only attend, Kitty, and not talk so much, I'll tell you all my ideas about Looking-glass House. First, there's the room you can see through the glass—that's just the same as our drawing-room, only the things go the other way. I can see all of it when I get upon a chair—all but the bit just behind the fireplace. Oh! I do so wish I could see *that* bit! I want so much to know whether they've a fire in the winter: you never *can* tell, you know, unless our fire smokes, and then smoke comes up in that room too—but that may be only pretence, just to make it look as if they had a fire. Well then, the books are something like our books, only the words go the wrong way; I know *that*, because I've held up one of our books to the glass, and then they hold up one in the other room."

Chess and Dominoes

Tweedledum and Tweedledee were playing chess, and they asked Alice if she wanted to join them.

"I'm sick and tired of chess!" she said. "Everything in this world is about chess. I don't know how you can play any more of it!"

"We also have dominoes," said Tweedledum. "We could play that instead."

"No, thank you," said Alice. "I really don't feel like playing any sort of game at the moment."

As she was talking to Tweedledum, Tweedledee had been laying out the dominoes on the chessboard, so that each domino covered exactly two squares of the board. He was able to place 32 dominoes, so that every square of the board was covered.

"That's no challenge," said Tweedledum, looking over at it. He shook the dominoes off the board, retrieved a large pair of scissors from his pocket, and then cut off two opposite corner squares of the board. "Now see if you can cover all the squares with 31 dominoes."

Could it be done?

Shifting Words 5 ᴥ

The Mad Hatter has shifted forward the letters of the following Lewis Carroll quotation by a certain number of places alphabetically. Can you deduce the shift and identify the quotation?

Juct, juct, juct. Cuarj znk lgrr tkbkx iusk zu gt ktj?

Card Tricks ꩜

Alice had been wandering around in the Royal Gardens when she came upon the Royal Gardeners: the Two of Hearts, the Five of Hearts, and the Seven of Hearts. She struck up a conversation with them, and the Five of Hearts asked if she would like to see a card trick. She agreed, half expecting the trick to involve the three gardeners themselves, but in fact he had with him his own small pack of cards. He handed a pile of them to Alice.

"Rotate one of the cards and then put it back in the pack," he said.

Alice looked through the cards. She saw a total of seven hearts, seven clubs, and seven spades. For each of these suits, she had the ace, three, five, six, seven, eight, and nine. There were also two diamonds: the three of diamonds and the seven of diamonds. She turned round the three of diamonds and then handed the stack back to the gardener. He looked through them quickly.

"You chose the three of diamonds!" he said triumphantly.

"But I made sure the card would look identical when rotated, and it did!" exclaimed Alice, confused as to how he had successfully identified her card.

How did the trick work, and why did he give Alice that particular selection of cards?

Card Watching

"The Queen of Hearts is looking for you," the Cheshire Cat told Alice, "with all of her eyes."

"All of her eyes?" Alice asked. "Doesn't she just have two?"

"Oh, but have you never seen a deck of cards before?" the Cheshire Cat enquired enigmatically.

"Of course I have!" said Alice indignantly.

"Then you ought to know as well as anyone that there are four eyes on the Queen of Hearts."

Alice considered this. She was sure each of the Queen's faces had two eyes, but then she remembered that there were two faces on each face card.

"I see what you mean," she replied.

"But here's something you probably haven't considered before. How many eyes are visible in a standard pack of cards?"

House of Cards

Alice was daydreaming about building a giant house of cards from some of the playing cards in Wonderland. She had tried building a house of cards before, with a pack of cards her sister had given her. The first layer had had 6 cards in it, leaning against each other in pairs. Then there were 2 cards placed flat across the tops. Above that were 4 more cards, also leaning against each other in pairs, with 1 card placed flat across them, and then a final pair leaning against each other at the top. Alice's tower looked like this:

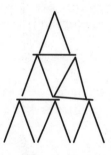

She had started again on a larger house of cards, but Dinah came in and knocked it all over, and she didn't have the heart to start again.

Building a house of cards in the same way that Alice once did, what is the maximum number of layers you can make if you start with a standard 52-card deck, so that it starts with an upright layer and finishes with an upright pair at the top? Count both upright and flat layers in the total layer count.

Blind Man's Bluff

Tweedledum had blindfolded Tweedledee, and then handed him a pack of cards in which, he explained, 16 were face up and the other 36 were face down.

"Sort these into two piles," he said, "so that each pile has the same number of face-up cards."

Tweedledee thought for several minutes, and then came up with a solution. How did he do it, without being able to see any of the cards?

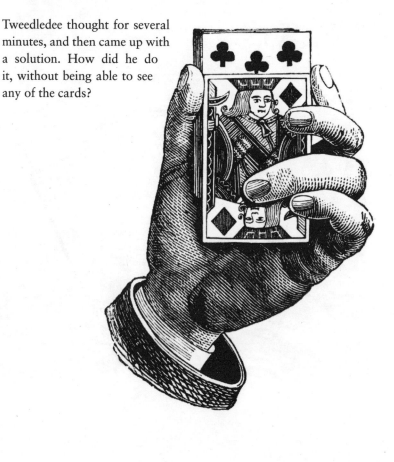

Four of a Kind ❧

Tweedledum and Tweedledee each had a standard pack of 52 cards. They put both packs together into one larger pile between them, and both began drawing vast quantities of cards until finally Tweedledum said, "Bingo!"

He showed Tweedledee that he had four twos.

What's the lowest number of cards Tweedledum would have had to draw from the two packs to guarantee that he got four of a kind?

"The Walrus and the Carpenter": Part Two

Excerpt from *Through the Looking-Glass, and What Alice Found There*, chapter IV

The eldest Oyster looked at him,
 But never a word he said:
The eldest Oyster winked his eye,
 And shook his heavy head—
Meaning to say he did not choose
 To leave the oyster-bed.

But four young oysters hurried up,
 All eager for the treat:
Their coats were brushed, their faces washed,
 Their shoes were clean and neat—
And this was odd, because, you know,
 They hadn't any feet.

Four other Oysters followed them,
 And yet another four;
And thick and fast they came at last,
 And more, and more, and more—
All hopping through the frothy waves,
 And scrambling to the shore.

The Walrus and the Carpenter
 Walked on a mile or so,
And then they rested on a rock
 Conveniently low:
And all the little Oysters stood
 And waited in a row.

'The time has come,' the Walrus said,
    'To talk of many things:
Of shoes—and ships—and sealing-wax—
    Of cabbages—and kings—
And why the sea is boiling hot—
    And whether pigs have wings.'

'But wait a bit,' the Oysters cried,
    'Before we have our chat;
For some of us are out of breath,
    And all of us are fat!'
'No hurry!' said the Carpenter.
    They thanked him much for that.

'A loaf of bread,' the Walrus said,
    'Is what we chiefly need:
Pepper and vinegar besides
    Are very good indeed—
Now if you're ready, Oysters dear,
    We can begin to feed.'

'But not on us!' the Oysters cried,
    Turning a little blue.
'After such kindness, that would be
    A dismal thing to do!'
'The night is fine,' the Walrus said.
    'Do you admire the view?

POEM CONCLUDES ON PAGE 156

Even More Sense and Nonsense

A passage from *Through the Looking-Glass* has been encoded by swapping pairs of letters according to a particular rule. Can you work out how it has been altered, and reveal the original passage?

Mld, sviv, blf hvv, rg gzpvh zoo gsv ifmmrmt blf xzm wl, gl pvvk rm gsv hznv kozxv. Ru blf dzmg gl tvg hlnvdsviv vohv, blf nfhg ifm zg ovzhg gdrxv zh uzhg zh gszg!

Rebus 1

Can you identify the Carrollian phrase clued by the following?

POSSIBLE
POSSIBLE
POSSIBLE
POSSIBLE
POSSIBLE
POSSIBLE

THINGS

Mad Multiplication

"How many people are there in Wonderland?" Alice asked the Cheshire Cat. "I'm sure I see at least one new person every ten minutes."

"People?" asked the Cheshire Cat. "We're not all people, you know. In fact, most of us aren't."

The Cheshire Cat looked rather offended, so Alice quickly apologized. "I'm terribly sorry," said Alice. "I didn't mean anything by it. I just wondered how many animals and, um, things lived in Wonderland."

The Cat harrumphed. "Fine. I shall forgive you if you are able to answer a simple question: What would you get if you multiplied together in one giant multiplication the number of hands that each Wonderland resident has?"

Alice frowned. "But you haven't told me how many residents there are! How could I possibly work that out?"

The Cat shook his head. "Alas. It would seem you are guilty of repeating your previous mistake."

What was the answer?

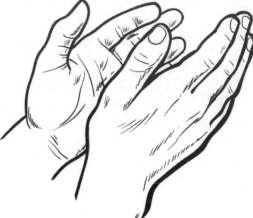

Wonderland Zigzag 1 &

Can you fill in the gaps in the following zigzag puzzle, which starts and ends with a Wonderland-themed word? The last two letters of each word must be the same as the first two of the next one.

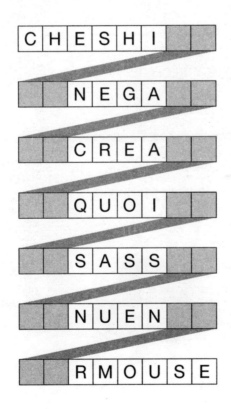

Nonsense Pairs

Can you delete one letter in each of the following letter pairs to reveal the names of some Wonderland characters?

QA BU HE KE IN OR UF SH ME AO RL ET SP

RM EA DI RH AB OT IT EC RS

CA EL IN MC EL

ML AO RA VC HI NH EA RT ES

NT UW EM RE DR LI EA VD EX ME

Letter Soup ✎

The names of three Wonderland characters are jumbled up in this letter soup. Can you identify them?

e
e e L h
d l c T
d d w
m w c
u u
e c A
e D S
s I

Muddled Testimonies ❧

There were three witnesses at the trial of the Knave of Hearts: the March Hare, the White Rabbit, and Bill the Lizard. The trouble was that the trial was very badly organized, so all three witnesses kept talking over each other, and it was very hard to work out who was saying what.

Each witness claimed to have seen the Knave of Hearts on the day of the crime: only one of them claimed to have seen him eating the tarts, one of the others had seen him sleeping, and one had seen him reading a book. One of them had seen him in the royal gardens, one had seen him in the Duchess's kitchen, and one had seen him standing beneath a giant mushroom. And one of them had seen him at 9 a.m., one at 2 p.m., and one at 7 p.m.

Alice was also able to make out the following:
- Bill the Lizard had seen the Knave of Hearts before he was at the giant mushroom.
- The Knave of Hearts was reading a book in the afternoon.
- The Knave of Hearts was sleeping in the Duchess's kitchen.
- The March Hare saw him after he'd been to the royal gardens.
- The White Rabbit saw him five hours before he ate the tarts.
- The Knave of Hearts did not eat the tarts in the royal gardens.

Based on this information, can you deduce who saw the Knave of Hearts doing what, where and when?

The Road to the Palace

Alice was on her way to the palace to play croquet with the Queen of Hearts. As she was walking, she saw a very strange party approaching her. As they got nearer, she saw that it was led by the Cheshire Cat. With him were six people, among whom she recognized the Duchess and the Hatter. Each of these people had with them six birds, and each bird was carrying six mice. When she got really close, she could see that each mouse was carrying six insects.

"How odd," Alice thought, though she was not nearly as surprised as she would have been if she had only just arrived in Wonderland and had not become quite accustomed to seeing strange sights such as these.

In total, counting every living being mentioned, how many were going to the palace?

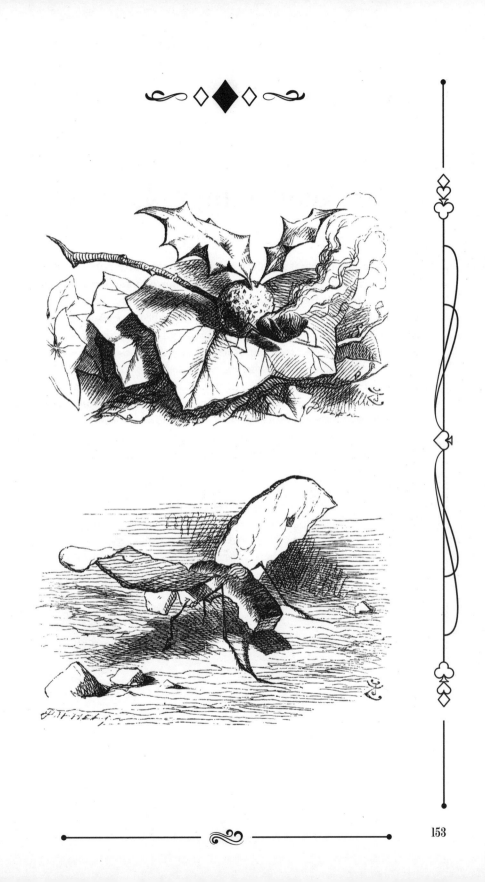

The Giant Puppy 🐋

Alice thought that she must at that moment be very small. Alternatively, the puppy she was looking at was much, much bigger than even any fully grown dog she'd ever seen. Despite this, it didn't look too dangerous: it sat watching her with wide brown eyes and then began reaching its paw out toward her. She had half a mind to start playing with it, but the other half of her mind was slightly afraid that it might trample her, or even eat her if it was hungry. So she decided it would be best to make an escape.

She picked up a stick, which sent the puppy quite mad with excitement, and it lurched terrifyingly toward her. In a great hurry, she leaned back and threw the stick into the nearby woods with all her might, and the puppy went charging off after it.

She turned in relief and began to walk away when all of a sudden a large grin materialized beside her, and shortly after it the rest of the Cheshire Cat chose to join it.

"A good throw," he observed. "I should say that you had that puppy running as far into the woods as it was possible to go."

"And how far is that?" Alice asked. She thought that if it really had been a long throw, she might report it back to her sister.

The Cheshire Cat grinned. "You tell me. What's the farthest it's possible to go into the woods?"

"The Walrus and the Carpenter": Part Three

Excerpt from *Through the Looking-Glass, and What Alice Found There*, chapter IV

'It was so kind of you to come!
    And you are very nice!'
The Carpenter said nothing but
    'Cut us another slice:
I wish you were not quite so deaf—
    I've had to ask you twice!'

'It seems a shame,' the Walrus said,
    'To play them such a trick,
After we've brought them out so far,
    And made them trot so quick!'
The Carpenter said nothing but
    'The butter's spread too thick!'

'I weep for you,' the Walrus said,
    'I deeply sympathize.'
With sobs and tears he sorted out
    Those of the largest size,
Holding his pocket-handkerchief
    Before his streaming eyes.

'O Oysters,' said the Carpenter.
　　　'You've had a pleasant run!
Shall we be trotting home again?'
　　　But answer came there none—
And this was scarcely odd, because
　　　They'd eaten every one."

Rebus 2 ❧

Can you identify the Carrollian phrase clued by the following?

THE

G-GLA**LOOK**SS

A Slow Race

The Hatter was trying to teach Tweedledum and Tweedledee some patience. They were both planning to come to the tea party that day, and he told them that the brother whose trousers were the last to touch their seat would get the most cakes.

Knowing this, the brothers wandered very slowly in the direction of the tea party; so slowly, in fact, that they were hardly moving. Alice came upon them shuffling forward in this strange way and asked them what was going on. They explained their predicament to her, and she made a suggestion that soon had them racing to get to the tea party.

What did Alice suggest?

Lewis Carroll's Bookshelf

There are four closed books stacked in a pile on Lewis Carroll's bookshelf: *Alice's Adventures in Wonderland*; *Through the Looking-Glass, and What Alice Found There*; *Phantasmagoria and Other Poems*; and *The Hunting of the Snark*. One of these books was published in 1865, one in 1869, one in 1871, and one in 1876. The following is also true:

- *Through the Looking-Glass* is touching the book that was published in 1876.
- The book published in 1865 is higher in the stack than *Phantasmagoria and Other Poems*.
- The book at the bottom of the stack has the same number of words in its full title as the book published in 1865.
- The book published in 1869 is earlier in the alphabet than the book at the top of the stack.
- *Phantasmagoria and Other Poems* is not touching the book published in 1876.
- *The Hunting of the Snark* has at least one book above it.

Based on this information, can you deduce when each book was published and where it is in the stack? (In this puzzle it is important to note that the leading word *The* is ignored in establishing the alphabetical order of the titles.)

Labyrinth 1 ❧

Can you help Alice find her way through the circular labyrinth, avoiding all of the dead ends along the way?

Mathematical Mushroom 2

Can you fill the boxes in this mathematical mushroom with numbers from the range 1 to 9? Each connected number adds together to make the total given at the end of that line, and no number can be repeated within a line.

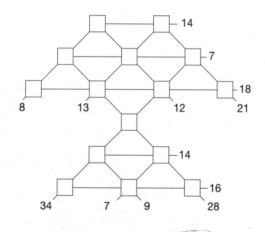

Guessing the Hand 1 ❧

Tweedledum is holding three cards:

- There is a jack to the left of a queen.
- There's a queen to the right of a club.
- There's a diamond to the left of a club.
- There's a diamond next to a queen.
- There's a diamond on the far right.

What are his cards?

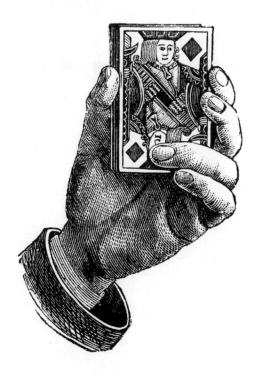

Rebus 3

Can you identify the Carrollian word clued by the following?

W^{LI CE}

DERL&

Seating Arrangements

There are five people attending a Tea Party: the Hatter, the March Hare, the Dormouse, Alice, and the White Rabbit. There are also five seats in a row along a bench, and so they all move to sit down, but the Hatter stops them.

"Wait!" he says. "There's a seating plan!"

"Well, then, where you do want us to sit?" the White Rabbit asked anxiously.

"Hmm…" said the Hatter. "Well, I remember that the Dormouse isn't next to Alice or me. Alice isn't next to the March Hare, and neither is the White Rabbit. The White Rabbit isn't next to me, the March Hare is next to me on my right, and Alice is somewhere to the left of the White Rabbit."

Can you deduce where they should all sit in relation to one other?

"A Mad Tea-Party"
Excerpt from *Alice's Adventures in Wonderland,* chapter VII

"I want a clean cup," interrupted the Hatter: "let's all move one place on."

He moved on as he spoke, and the Dormouse followed him: the March Hare moved into the Dormouse's place, and Alice rather unwillingly took the place of the March Hare. The Hatter was the only one who got any advantage from the change: and Alice was a good deal worse off than before, as the March Hare had just upset the milk-jug into his plate.

Alice did not wish to offend the Dormouse again, so she began very cautiously: "But I don't understand. Where did they draw the treacle from?"

"You can draw water out of a water-well," said the Hatter; "so I should think you could draw treacle out of a treacle-well—eh, stupid?"

"But they were *in* the well," Alice said to the Dormouse, not choosing to notice this last remark.

"Of course they were," said the Dormouse; "—well in."

This answer so confused poor Alice, that she let the Dormouse go on for some time without interrupting it.

"They were learning to draw," the Dormouse went on, yawning and rubbing its eyes, for it was getting very sleepy; "and they drew all manner of things—everything that begins with an M—"

"Why with an M?" said Alice.

"Why not?" said the March Hare.

Alice was silent.

The Dormouse had closed its eyes by this time, and was going off into a doze; but, on being pinched by the Hatter, it woke up again with a little shriek, and went on: "—that begins with an M, such as mouse-traps, and the moon, and memory, and muchness—you know you say things are 'much of a muchness'—did you ever see such a thing as a drawing of a muchness?"

"Really, now you ask me," said Alice, very much confused, "I don't think—"

"Then you shouldn't talk," said the Hatter.

This piece of rudeness was more than Alice could bear: she got up in great disgust, and walked off; the Dormouse fell asleep instantly, and neither of the others took the least notice of her going, though she looked back once or twice, half hoping that they would call after her: the last time she saw them, they were trying to put the Dormouse into the teapot.

Mathematical Mushroom 3

Can you fill the boxes in this mathematical mushroom with numbers from the range 1 to 9? Each connected number adds together to make the total given at the end of that line, and no number can be repeated within a line.

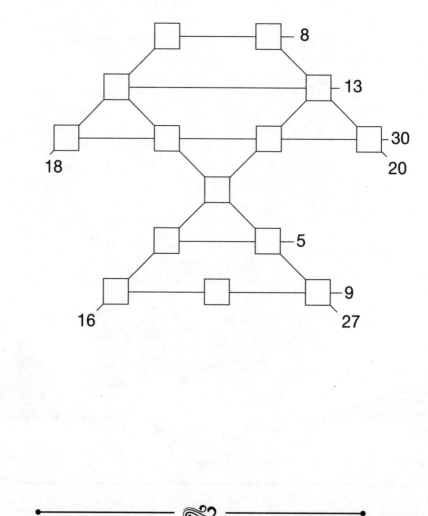

Rebus 4 ✎

Can you identify the Carrollian phrase clued by the following?

T
H
E

RABBIT

Guessing the Hand 2 ✒

Tweedledee is holding four cards:

- Reading them from left to right, the sum of the first three equals the fourth.
- Two cards have the same value, and are not adjacent.
- Two cards have the same suit, and are not adjacent.
- There's a heart to the left of a two.
- There's a three to the right of a heart.
- There's a spade to the right of a diamond.
- There's a heart next to a two.
- The farthest-left card is even.

What are his cards?

Wonderland Word Catalogue

The following words all have a Wonderland-related word in common. Can you identify it?

- Alley
- Burglar
- Fat
- Flap
- House
- Jungle

Mutual Words ❧

Can you fill in each of the gaps below by finding a Wonderland-related word that can follow the first word in each pair and precede the second, making two two-word phrases in each case? Each phrase should be reasonably expected to be found in a dictionary.

FIELD ____ MAT

SPREAD ____ EYE

BEAUTY ____ BEE

SITTING ____ BOAT

NEST ____ TIMER

PRIMORDIAL ____ SPOON

Mixed Chapters 1

Can you unscramble these anagrammed chapter titles of *Alice's Adventures in Wonderland*? The length of each word in the chapter title is given.

If this is too tricky, solve the Split Titles puzzles on pages 64 and 70 to find the original titles.

- Coagulated casual enchanter. (3, 6, 4, 3, 1, 4, 4)

- Grotesque, conquered hunt. (3, 6, 7, 6)

- Littlest ideal babblers hint. (3, 6, 5, 1, 6, 4)

- The toothless wart. (3, 5, 3, 5)

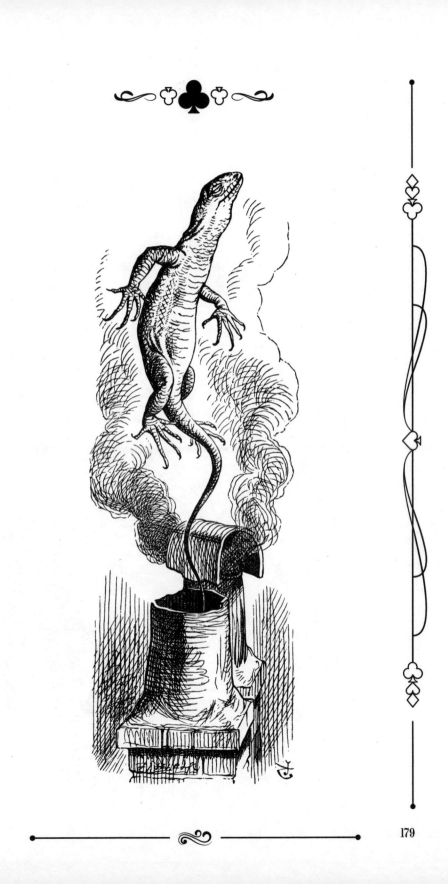

Word Changer 1

Can you change LORY into KING in just 6 steps, changing only one letter at each step and without rearranging the letters? Each step must be to a regular English word.

LORY

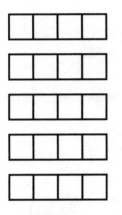

KING

For an extra challenge, can you find a way to change LORY into KING in just five steps, using an obscure word?

And then can you do it in four steps, with even more obscure words?

Mixed Chapters 2 &

Can you unscramble these anagrammed chapter titles of *Alice's Adventures in Wonderland*? The length of each word in the chapter title is given.

If this is too tricky, solve the Split Titles puzzles on pages 64 and 70 to find the original titles.

- Alive Decencies. (6, 8)

- Dapper pigpen. (3, 3, 6)

- Hot wobble in hatred. (4, 3, 6, 4)

- Loather of poets. (3, 4, 2, 5)

A Game for One 1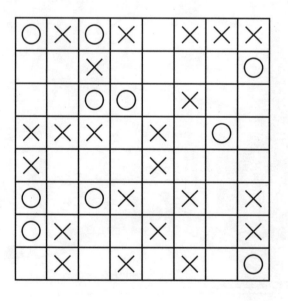

Alice came upon the following partially completed game, and felt that it would be quite wrong to continue without finishing it off.

She must place an X or an O into every empty square, so that *no* lines of four or more Xs or Os are made in any direction, including diagonally. How should she complete the game? (There is no requirement to use an equal number of Xs and Os.)

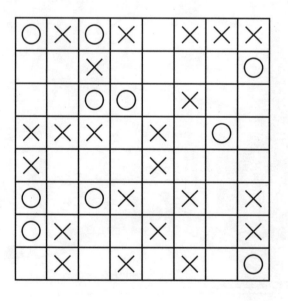

One Growing Potion ❧

In a cupboard of glasses in the Duchess's kitchen, Alice came across 1,000 bottles, each of which had a label saying: Drink Me. She knew that exactly one of these bottles contained the growing potion she was looking for, while the rest would have no effect on her. A single sip of the growing potion would be enough to make her grow only slightly. She wanted to grow a lot, however, and since she didn't much like the taste of any of the potions, she wanted to find the bottle with the growing potion while drinking as little overall quantity of the potions as possible.

What is the fewest number of sips it would take her to identify the precise bottle which contains the growing potion?

"Pig and Pepper"

Excerpt from *Alice's Adventures in Wonderland,*
chapter VI

"Please would you tell me," said Alice, a little timidly, for she was not quite sure whether it was good manners for her to speak first, "why your cat grins like that?"

"It's a Cheshire cat," said the Duchess, "and that's why. Pig!"

She said the last word with such sudden violence that Alice quite jumped; but she saw in another moment that it was addressed to the baby, and not to her, so she took courage, and went on again:

"I didn't know that Cheshire cats always grinned; in fact, I didn't know that cats *could* grin."

"They all can," said the Duchess; "and most of 'em do."

"I don't know of any that do," Alice said very politely, feeling quite pleased to have got into a conversation.

"You don't know much," said the Duchess; "and that's a fact."

Alice did not at all like the tone of this remark, and thought it would be as well to introduce some other subject of conversation. While she was trying to fix on one, the cook took the cauldron of soup off the fire, and at once set to work throwing everything within her reach at the Duchess and the baby—the fire-irons came first; then followed a shower of saucepans, plates, and dishes.

The Duchess took no notice of them even when they hit her; and the baby was howling so much already, that it was quite impossible to say whether the blows hurt it or not.

"Oh, *please* mind what you're doing!" cried Alice, jumping up and down in an agony of terror. "Oh, there goes his *precious* nose", as an unusually large saucepan flew close by it, and very nearly carried it off.

"If everybody minded their own business," the Duchess said in a hoarse growl, "the world would go round a deal faster than it does."

"Which would *not* be an advantage," said Alice, who felt very glad to get an opportunity of showing off a little of her knowledge. "Just think of what work it would make with the day and night! You see the earth takes twenty-four hours to turn round on its axis—"

"Talking of axes," said the Duchess, "chop off her head!"

Alice glanced rather anxiously at the cook, to see if she meant to take the hint; but the cook was busily stirring the soup, and seemed not to be listening, so she went on again: "Twenty-four hours, I *think*; or is it twelve? I—"

"Oh, don't bother *me*," said the Duchess; "I never could abide figures!"

Slaying the Jabberwock ❧

Can you fill in the blanks in these lines from the poem "Jabberwocky" and then take the first letters in order from top to bottom and spell out a Wonderland-related word?

So rested he by the _____ tree

And the mome raths _____

And _____ in uffish thought he stood

_____ gyre and gimble in the wade

Twas brillig, and the _____ toves

Came whiffling through the _____ wood

One, two! _____, two! And through and through!

_____ frabjous day! Callooh! Callay!

_____ time the manxome foe he sought

Rearranging Humpty Dumpty

The poem "Humpty Dumpty" consists of 26 words. This means that each word of the poem can be assigned a different letter.

To decode the following quotation from the character Humpty Dumpty, you will need to assign each word of the poem a letter of the alphabet in order. So, starting with the first line, Humpty = A, Dumpty = B, sat = C, on = D, a = E, wall = F, and so on.

Now, using this assignment of words to letters, can you decode the following?

Put Dumpty a the/ had/ men the a/ Humpty/ put king's all on/ had king's/ all a Humpty the the/ a men the king's/ put Dumpty Humpty king's/ had/ sat Dumpty king's king's the a/ had king's/ king's king's/ all a Humpty the.

Note that some words will have multiple letters assigned to them (since those words repeat), so you'll have to use the context to work out which letter is meant.

Chessboard Assembly 1

Each square of a chessboard is identified by referring to its column letter, from A to H, and its row number, from 1 to 8. The first 5 rows and 5 columns of a particular chessboard have been cut up into separate squares, jumbled together, and then laid out again. Each square is marked with the original row and column it came from.

Given that no row or column contains two squares that have either the same number or the same letter, can you complete this chart showing where each original square has been placed?

B	C	4	E	D1
		5	C	
D4	1		A	C5
	4	C		
C2	5	D	1	4

Word Changer 2 ❧

Can you change LION into HARE in just 5 steps, changing only one letter at each step and without rearranging the letters? Each step must be to a regular English word, although the first step is to a relatively obscure literary word.

LION

HARE

Labyrinth 2

Alice has been swept up by her pool of tears. Can you help her to find her way through from the top to the bottom of the labyrinth she has created?

Days and Days ❧

It was easy to lose track of time in Wonderland. Sometimes hours passed in minutes, and sometimes seconds took days.

"What day of the week is it?" Alice asked the Caterpillar one day.

"When the day after tomorrow is yesterday, then today will be as far from Monday as today was from Monday when the day before yesterday was tomorrow," said the Caterpillar.

So what day was it?

Eating at the Tea-Party ❧

There was a big platter of cucumber sandwiches at the Tea Party.
- The Hatter ate less than the Hare.
- Tweedledum ate more than Tweedledee
- Tweedledee ate more than the Hare, but less than the Dormouse.

Who ate the second-fewest sandwiches?

Alternate Letters 1

Can you identify the following Wonderland characters when only every other letter of their name is given?

_U E_ O_ H A_T_

_H_S_I E _A_

_A_C_ H_R_

_W_E_L_D_E

The Hole 

"How curious!" thought Alice one day, as she came upon a sudden hole in the road.

"Why, who would dig a hole in such a place? It is a most unremarkable spot to have chosen, and I can see no rhyme or reason as to its location.

"And yet it is an interesting hole, if holes can indeed be interesting (which I do think they can), for its sides are so perfectly cut into the surrounding soil.

"Indeed, I see that whoever who dug this hole was so proud of the hole that they have noted down its dimensions.

"Given that the hole claims to be 4 feet wide, 3 feet long, and 5 feet deep, what, I wonder, is the volume of the soil in this hole?"

Can you answer Alice's question?

"Queen Alice"

Excerpt from *Through the Looking-Glass, and What Alice Found There*, chapter IX

"Can you do Addition?" the White Queen asked. "What's one and one and one and one and one and one and one and one and one and one?"

"I don't know," said Alice. "I lost count."

"She can't do Addition," the Red Queen interrupted. "Can you do Subtraction? Take nine from eight."

"Nine from eight I can't, you know," Alice replied very readily: "but—"

"She can't do Subtraction," said the White Queen. "Can you do Division? Divide a loaf by a knife—what's the answer to that?"

"I suppose—" Alice was beginning, but the Red Queen answered for her. "Bread-and-butter, of course. Try another Subtraction sum. Take a bone from a dog: what remains?"

Alice considered. "The bone wouldn't remain, of course, if I took it—and the dog wouldn't remain; it would come to bite me—and I'm sure *I* shouldn't remain!"

"Then you think nothing would remain?" said the Red Queen.

"I think that's the answer."

"Wrong, as usual," said the Red Queen: "the dog's temper would remain."

"But I don't see how—"

"Why, look here!" the Red Queen cried. "The dog would lose its temper, wouldn't it!"

"Perhaps it would," Alice replied cautiously.

"Then if the dog went away, its temper would remain!" the Queen exclaimed triumphantly.

Alice said, as gravely as she could, "They might go

different ways." But she couldn't help thinking to herself, "What dreadful nonsense we *are* talking!"

"She can't do sums a *bit*!" the Queens said together, with great emphasis.

"Can *you* do sums?" Alice said, turning suddenly on the White Queen, for she didn't like being found fault with so much.

The Queen gasped and shut her eyes. "I can do Addition," she said, "if you give me time—but I can't do Subtraction, under *any* circumstances!"

"Of course you know your A B C?" said the Red Queen.

"To be sure I do," said Alice.

"So do I," the White Queen whispered: "we'll often say it over together, dear. And I'll tell you a secret—I can read words of one letter! Isn't *that* grand! However, don't be discouraged. You'll come to it in time."

Here the Red Queen began again. "Can you answer useful questions?" she said. "How is bread made?"

"I know *that*!" Alice cried eagerly. "You take some flour—"

"Where do you pick the flower?" the White Queen asked. "In a garden, or in the hedges?"

"Well, it isn't *picked* at all," Alice explained: "it's *ground*—"

"How many acres of ground?" said the White Queen. "You mustn't leave out so many things."

"Fan her head!" the Red Queen anxiously interrupted. "She'll be feverish after so much thinking." So they set to work and fanned her with bunches of leaves, till she had to beg them to leave off, it blew her hair about so.

Attacking Knights 1

Six different types of knight are to be placed onto a 6×6 board. Each type of knight is identified by a letter, from A to F.

Only one knight can be placed into any square, and some knights are already on the board. Can you replace the remaining knights so that every row and column contains one of each type of knight, A to F?

Also, knights must not be able to attack another knight of the same type in a single move. As in chess, this consists of moving one square horizontally and two squares vertically, or two squares horizontally and one square vertically. Therefore no two matching letters can be a single knight's move apart from one another.

Can you complete the board?

E		D	F		A
B					C
F					B
C		A	B		F

Wonderland Zigzag 2

Can you fill in the gaps in the following zigzag puzzle, which starts and ends with a Wonderland-themed word? The last two letters of each word are the same as the first two of the following one.

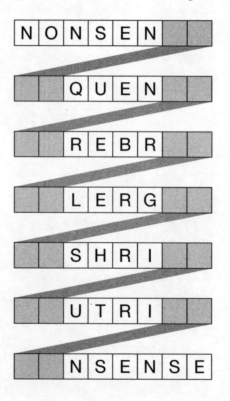

The Slow Climb

The White Rabbit was trying to climb back up out of a rabbit hole so as to leave Wonderland. The rabbit hole was 60 m high, and the Rabbit was able to climb up 6 m every ten minutes—but then his arms would give out and he'd sink back down 4 m again.

How long did it take him to climb the whole 60 m?

Alternate Letters 2

Can you identify the following Wonderland characters when only every other letter of their name is given?

_H_T_ R_B_I_

_O_K _U_T_E

_W_E_L_D_M

_U_P_Y _U_P_Y

Rebus 5

Can you identify the Wonderland resident clued by the following?

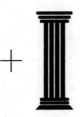 +ER

+

A Game for One 2 ❧

Alice came upon the following partially completed game, and felt that it would be quite wrong to continue without finishing it off.

She must place an X or an O into every empty square, so that *no* lines of four or more Xs or Os are made in any direction, including diagonally.

How should she complete the game? (There is no requirement to use an equal number of Xs and Os.)

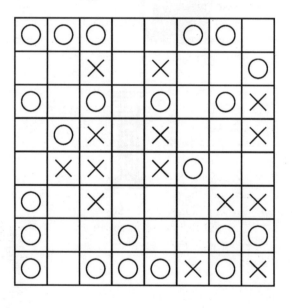

The Jackdaw's Puzzle

Alice came presently upon a large dining table. She decided it must be a dining table, for it was set with all manner of knives, forks, spoons, and other cutlery items, some of which Alice was sure she had never seen before, and she could not begin to guess their use. There was not a morsel of food or drink on the table, which was rather a disappointment to Alice, who by this time was feeling rather hungry.

Alice was wondering whether to wait or carry on, when unexpectedly a jackdaw in a very small top hat appeared and spoke to Alice, saying, "Well, here's a pretty pickle. If you can help me with this teaser, I will have the table filled with food." Alice gladly signalled her desire to help, at which point the jackdaw continued: "My wife and I have been discussing this problem all day. She heard it from a raven, and he heard it from a crow, but you know how they are and the answer had been forgotten before the question had been solved. It's such a shame. I do hope you can help. The problem is rather simple, in fact, so I am sure you will be able to tell me what I imagine I already know."

This was rather a confusing statement, but to Alice's relief the actual problem was much simpler:

"In a far-off kingdom, boys and girls are equally likely to be born. But if the king then decrees that no couple can have any further children, once a boy is born to them, what effect will this have? In the future, will there be more girls than boys, or more boys than girls?"

How should Alice respond?

Word Changer 3

Can you change ALICE into STORY in just 6 steps, changing only one letter at each step and without rearranging the letters? Each step must be to a regular English word.

ALICE

STORY

Mathematical Mushroom 4 🐛

Can you fill the boxes in this mathematical mushroom with numbers from the range 1 to 9? Each connected number adds together to make the total given at the end of that line, and no number can be repeated within a line.

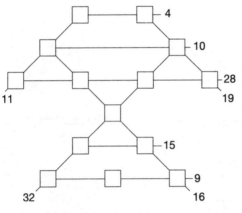

Labyrinth 3 🌿

Can you help Alice find her way across the croquet ground from top to bottom, avoiding all of the dead ends along the way?

Word Changer 4

Can you change SHEEP into FLOCK in just 6 steps, changing only one letter at each step and without rearranging the letters? Each step must be to a regular English word.

SHEEP

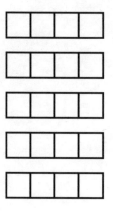

FLOCK

Rebus 6 ❧

Can you identify the Wonderland resident clued by the following rebus?

Attacking Knights 2 ❧

Seven different types of knight are to be placed onto a 7×7 board. Each type of knight is identified by a letter, from A to G.

Only one knight can be placed into any square, and some knights are already on the board. Can you replace the remaining knights so that every row and column contains one of each type of knight, A to G?

Also, knights must not be able to attack another knight of the same type in a single move. As in chess, this consists of moving one square horizontally and two squares vertically, or two squares horizontally and one square vertically. Therefore no two matching letters can be a single knight's move apart from one another.

Can you complete the board?

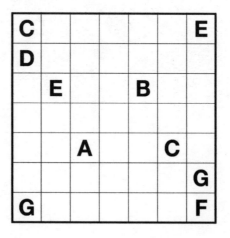

"Pig and Pepper"
Excerpt from *Alice's Adventures in Wonderland,*
chapter VI

"Do you play croquet with the Queen to-day?"

"I should like it very much," said Alice, "but I haven't been invited yet."

"You'll see me there," said the Cat, and vanished.

Alice was not much surprised at this, she was getting so used to queer things happening. While she was looking at the place where it had been, it suddenly appeared again.

"By-the-bye, what became of the baby?" said the Cat. "I'd nearly forgotten to ask."

"It turned into a pig," Alice quietly said, just as if it had come back in a natural way.

"I thought it would," said the Cat, and vanished again.

Alice waited a little, half expecting to see it again, but it did not appear, and after a minute or two she walked on in the direction in which the March Hare was said to live. "I've seen hatters before," she said to herself; "the March Hare will be much the most interesting, and perhaps as this is May it won't be raving mad—at least not so mad as it was in March." As she said this, she looked up, and there was the Cat again, sitting on a branch of a tree.

"Did you say pig, or fig?" said the Cat.

"I said pig," replied Alice; "and I wish you wouldn't keep appearing and vanishing so suddenly: you make one quite giddy."

"All right," said the Cat; and this time it vanished quite slowly, beginning with the end of the tail, and ending with the grin, which remained some time after the rest of it had gone.

"Well! I've often seen a cat without a grin," thought Alice; "but a grin without a cat! It's the most curious thing I ever saw in all my life!"

Labyrinth 4

The Cheshire Cat hasn't given Alice very helpful directions. Can you help her find her way through the forest of sloping trees? She is currently at the top of the forest, and needs to make her way to the bottom.

Gaps in the Looking-Glass

Can you fill in each of the blanks in these *Through the Looking-Glass* chapter titles with one of the words from the righthand column?

Looking-Glass _____
The Garden of Live _____
Tweedledum and _____
_____ and Water
The _____ and the Unicorn
"It's my own _____"
Queen _____
Which dreamed _____?

Alice
Flowers
House
Invention
It
Lion
Tweedledee
Wool

Word Changer 5

Can you change HEART into SUITS in just 6 steps, changing only one letter at each step and without rearranging the letters? Each step must be to a regular English word.

HEART

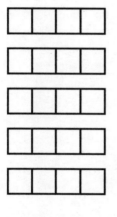

SUITS

Labyrinth 5 🐌

Alice comes upon a curious pentagonal labyrinth, which she is determined to explore. Can you help her find her way through, all the way from left to right?

Rebus 7 ❧

Can you identify the Wonderland resident clued by the following?

 − CK

+

Mixed Chapters 3

Can you unscramble these anagrammed chapter titles of *Alice's Adventures in Wonderland*? The length of each word in the chapter title is given.

If this is too tricky, solve the Split Titles puzzles on pages 64 and 70 to find the original titles.

- Adapt tame ray. (1, 3, 3-5)

- Farcical, pivotal dreamer. (6, 4, 1, 11)

- Idle quarrels blot. (7, 9)

- Mocker stutters hotly. (3, 4, 7, 5)

Chessboard Assembly 2 ✦

Each square of a chessboard is identified by referring to its column letter, from A to H, and its row number, from 1 to 8. The first 5 rows and 5 columns of a particular chessboard have been cut up into separate squares, jumbled together, and then laid out again. Each square is marked with the original row and column it came from.

Given that no row or column contains two squares that have either the same number or the same letter, can you complete this chart showing where each original square has been placed?

2	5	E	1	3
	E	2	D3	C4
C1	A3	D	4	
E	D	1	C	A

A Game for One 3 🔊

Alice came upon the following partially completed game, and felt that it would be quite wrong to continue without finishing it off.

She must place an X or an O into every empty square, so that *no* lines of four or more Xs or Os are made in any direction, including diagonally. How should she complete the game? (There is no requirement to use an equal number of Xs and Os.)

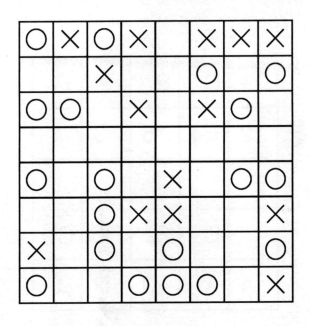

Chessboard Assembly 3

Each square of a chessboard is identified by referring to its column letter, from A to H, and its row number, from 1 to 8. The first 5 rows and 5 columns of a particular chessboard have been cut up into separate squares, jumbled together, and then laid out again. Each square is marked with the original row and column it came from.

Given that no row or column contains two squares that have either the same number or the same letter, can you complete this chart showing where each original square has been placed?

1	C	B	4	E
2	E4	5	3	
E				2
	D	E	B5	C
4	A	3	2	D

Rebus 8 🌰

Can you identify the Wonderland resident clued by the following rebus?

Attacking Knights 3

Eight different types of knight are to be placed onto a 8×8 board. Each type of knight is identified by a letter, from A to H.

Only one knight can be placed into any square, and some knights are already on the board. Can you replace the remaining knights so that every row and column contains one of each type of knight, A to H?

Also, knights must not be able to attack another knight of the same type in a single move. As in chess, this consists of moving one square horizontally and two squares vertically, or two squares horizontally and one square vertically. Therefore no two matching letters can be a single knight's move apart from one another.

Can you complete the board?

B	F					H	C
H			E	D			F
		A			C		
	D					C	
	C					A	
		F			D		
A			G	C			E
D	A					E	B

Solutions

Time for Wonderland .... page 8
Twelve minutes past eleven.

Down the Rabbit Hole .... page 10

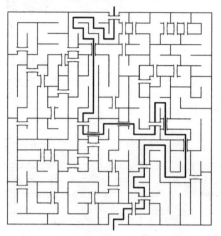

The Long Fall .... page 12
He had fallen off one of the lowest rungs of the ladder.

The Shrinking Bottle .... page 13
Alice would need to take six more sips after the original two. At this point she would be approximately 4.68 cm tall, and thus able to fit through the doorway.

Tweedledum and Tweedledee 1 .... page 14
Tweedledee. You know that at least one of them is lying about their name. Since they give different names, it cannot be the case that one of them is lying and the other is telling the truth for they would either both be called Tweedledum or both be called Tweedledee. So they must both be lying. Therefore, the one on the left must be Tweedledee, as he claims to be Tweedledum.

Too Big for Court .... page 19
She was 60 feet tall.

Remembering Forward .... page 20
Alice could easily *predict* the future. The hard part is predicting it *correctly*; she might well be wrong.

Solutions

Not Enough Tea . . . . page 22

Alice simply needs to pour the tea from the first and third cups into the sixth and eighth cups.

Not Enough Cake . . . . page 24

Twenty-eight.

Three Bottles . . . . page 25

The mushroom potion was in the smallest bottle and would make her shrink. The carrot potion was in the medium-sized bottle and would make her grow. The pepper potion was in the biggest bottle and would not change her height at all.

In The Kitchen . . . . page 27

One, if she takes a single vegetable from the basket marked POTATOES AND CARROTS. Whichever vegetable she removes from that basket, she can then deduce that all the vegetables in that basket are of that type. As the other two labels were also wrong, she could then deduce the contents of those too.

The Right Size . . . . page 28

Twelve: five bites of the cake and seven sips of the potion.

The Head Start . . . . page 32

The March Hare would win again. The first race demonstrated that he could run 100 m in the time it took the Hatter to run 90 m. So if they ran at the same speeds in the second race, they would draw level 10 m from the end. The Hare would then run the final 10 m more quickly than the Hatter, given that he was the faster runner.

The Not Lemonade . . . . page 34

Whatever it was that made Alice shrink must have been in the ice. The Cook drank her lemonade quickly, so the ice did not melt and she didn't ingest any of the shrinking substance. However, because Alice took much longer with hers, some of the ice melted while she drank and she ingested the substance that was in the ice.

Cake Selection . . . . page 35

Three: one carrot cake, one jam sponge, and one coffee cake.

The Sentence . . . . page 36

The Bandersnatch was his best option. If the Bandersnatch hadn't eaten in two months, it was probably either dead or very weak!

Solutions

Tweedledum and Tweedledee 2 .... page 39

Yes. The sentence *If I am Tweedledum, then my brother is Tweedledee* is false only if the speaker is Tweedledum and his brother is not Tweedledee. If the speaker were Tweedledee, then the sentence would be true, and Tweedledee cannot utter a true sentence, so the speaker cannot be Tweedledee and must be Tweedledum.

Too Many Queens .... page 42

Eight. There are only eight rows/columns on a chessboard, so we know the solution can't be more than eight. However, there are several ways to place eight queens so that they can't attack each other. For example:

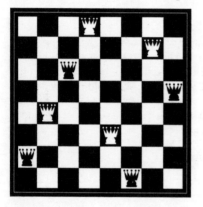

Shifting Words 1 .... page 44

Shift each letter five places backward in the alphabet, so A becomes V, B becomes W, C becomes X, and so on, to read: *Why is a raven like a writing-desk?*

Tea Party Invitations .... page 45

The names were anagrams of:
- Cheshire Cat
- Queen of Hearts
- White Rabbit
- Knave of Hearts
- Mock Turtle

Down the Stairs .... page 46

There must have been a minimum of eight steps in the staircase.

Solutions

Magic Mushrooms . . . . page 47

Alice's best bet is to take a mushroom from the basket marked TWO FOR SHRINKING. This basket either contains two mushrooms for growing, or one for growing and one for shrinking, meaning she has a ¾ chance of getting a growing mushroom. Using similar logic, the TWO FOR GROWING basket gives her only a ¼ chance of getting a growing mushroom, while the ONE FOR GROWING AND ONE FOR SHRINKING basket either has two for growing or two for shrinking, so her chances of getting a growing mushroom from this basket are ½.

A Pie Problem . . . . page 48

Alice put four pies each into the two smallest boxes and then put each of the two smallest boxes into one of the two biggest boxes. That way, each box contained exactly four pies.

The Hand that was Dealt . . . . page 51

The Dormouse held the two of hearts, the Hatter held the seven of diamonds, and the Hare held the queen of clubs.

Shifting Words 2 . . . . page 52

Shift each letter two places forward in the alphabet, so A becomes C, B becomes D, C becomes E, and so on, to read: *It doesn't matter which way you go... So long as I get somewhere.*

Tweedledum and Tweedledee 3 . . . . page 53

He sometimes lies. If he always lied, then both brothers' statements would be true. So that statement must be false, and therefore the other is true.

Strange Sequences 1 . . . . page 56

These are the last letters of months of the year from January to July. The next month is August, so the next letter is T.

The Three Pieces . . . . page 57

The bishop was in E3, the pawn was in A7, and the rook was in B4.

Looking Through the Looking Glass . . . . page 58

Since the books were themselves through the looking glass, their titles were written backward, and their letters differently spaced and punctuated. The books in English are:
- *To Kill A Mockingbird*, by Harper Lee
- *The Catcher in the Rye*, by J.D. Salinger
- *Finnegan's Wake*, by James Joyce
- *Alice's Adventures in Wonderland*, by Lewis Carroll

Solutions

Strange Sequences 2 .... page 59

These are the first letters of days of the week from Wednesday to Monday. The next day is Tuesday, so the next letter is T.

Shifting Words 3 .... page 60

Shift each letter eight places backward in the alphabet, so A becomes S, B becomes T, C becomes U, and so on, to read: *At least I know who I was when I got up this morning, but I think I must have been changed several times since then.*

Hidden Figures .... page 61

- Alice: It was during the origin*al ice* age.
- Dodo: Taekwon*do do*esn't require much equipment.
- Gryphon: I made an an*gry phon*e call.
- Walrus: The plan for rene*wal rus*hed us.
- Hatter: I found *that ter*rifying.

Character Match-up .... page 62

CHESHIRE	CAT
HUMPTY	DUMPTY
FROG	FOOTMAN
JUBJUB	BIRD
MAD	HATTER
MARCH	HARE
MOCK	TURTLE
RED	KING
WHITE	RABBIT

Too Many Legs .... page 64

There were 6 mice and 20 birds.

Stolen Vowels 1 .... page 68

CATERPILLAR
DORMOUSE
MAD HATTER
RED KING
WHITE RABBIT

Strange Sequences 3 .... page 70

These are the last letters of the shades of the rainbow, from red to indigo. The next is violet, so the next letter is T.

Solutions

These are the first letters of elements of the periodic table, from hydrogen to oxygen. The next element is fluorine, so the next letter is F.

BANDERSNATCH
CHESHIRE CAT
MOCK TURTLE
MARCH HARE
TWEEDLEDUM

A A T A A T	M D E P R Y	A MAD TEA-PARTY
A V C F O A A E P L A	D I E R M C T R I L R	ADVICE FROM A CATERPILLAR
L B T R U D I L	O S E Q A R L E	LOBSTER QUADRILLE
T E A B T E D A I T E I L	H R B I S N S L T L B L	THE RABBIT SENDS A LITTLE BILL
T E O K U T E S O Y	H M C T R L S T R	THE MOCK TURTLE'S STORY
T E U E S R Q E G O N	H Q E N C O U T R U D	THE QUEEN'S CROQUET GROUND

The pairs are: A + Lice, Cater + Pillar, Foot + Man, He + Arts, Hook + Ah, Mush + Room, Wonder + Land, and Uni + Corn. "Do" is the odd one out, as it can be paired with itself to make *dodo*.

A I E E I E C	L C S V D N E	ALICE'S EVIDENCE
D W T E A B T O E	O N H R B I H L	DOWN THE RABBIT HOLE
P G N P P E	I A D E P R	PIG AND PEPPER
T E A C S A E N A O G A E	H C U U R C A D L N T L	THE CAUCUS RACE AND A LONG TALE
T E O L F E R	H P O O T A S	THE POOL OF TEARS
W O T L T E A T	H S O E H T R S	WHO STOLE THE TARTS?

These are the first letters of whole numbers from one to seven. The next number is eight, so the next letter is E.

The jam sponges are the best, then the currant cakes, and then the chocolate cakes. Start by assuming that the second brother is telling the truth, and the chocolate cakes are not the worst. If this is true, then the first brother's statement is also true, because at least one half of the either/or claim is true, which is enough to make the claim as a whole true. As both

Solutions

brothers cannot be telling the truth, this means the second brother's claim must be false, and the chocolate cakes are the worst. In order for the first brother's claim to be true, it must be the case that the other half of his either/or claim is true: the jam sponges are the best. The currant cakes, which can be neither best nor worst, must be in the middle.

An Abundance of Tea

He would pour his 150th cup on the 17th day of the exercise.

In Other Words

The characters are:
- The Mad Hatter (loopy = mad, milliner = hatter)
- The March Hare (parade = march, leveret = hare)
- The Mock Turtle (ridicule = mock, reptile = turtle)
- The Caterpillar (feline = cat, um = er, column = pillar)

Changing Sizes

She ate the cake in the morning and it made her 300 cm tall. She drank the potion in the afternoon and it made her 50 cm tall. She ate the mushroom in the evening and it made her 150 cm tall.

The Wrong Names

Zero. If she was right about fourteen names, then she would also have to be right about the fifteenth.

Birds of a Feather

26.

A Sponge Shared

It would take Tweedledee an hour to eat the cake on his own. If it takes Tweedledum 30 minutes to eat the whole cake, then in ⅔ of the time—20 minutes—he must eat ⅔ of the cake. This means that in 20 minutes Tweedledee eats ⅓ of the cake, so it would take him three times that to eat the whole cake.

Madness and Nonsense

The Cheshire Cat could be right. If 30 per cent of Wonderland residents were a lot madder than the rest, then they could drag up the average so that the other 70 per cent were less mad than average. This works so long as the average is defined as the mean, as it usually is unless otherwise specified, and if madness can indeed be quantified.

Solutions

Shifting Words 4 . . . . page 95

Shift each letter eleven places forward in the alphabet, so A becomes L, B becomes M, C becomes N, and so on, to read: *Why, sometimes I've believed as many as six impossible things before breakfast.*

Too Big for the Kitchen . . . . page 98

12.16.

Before the Trial . . . . page 100

Thirteen.

Collecting Mushrooms . . . . page 101

No. If half the mushrooms have already taken her twice as long as they should have taken, then she's already out of time.

Tweedledum and Tweedledee 5 . . . . page 102

She could ask one of the brothers a question along the lines of: *If I asked your brother whether that was the way to the Royal Garden, would he say yes?* If it was the right way, then the lying brother would lie about the honest brother's answer and answer "no", and the honest brother would tell the truth about the honest brother's answer and also answer "no." If it was the wrong way, they would both say "yes" for the same reasons.

Plates of Cakes . . . . page 104

Twelve. There would need to be 91 cakes to make it to thirteen plates.

Talking Flowers . . . . page 105

The daisy was the shortest flower, and pink. The rose was the next tallest, and white. The tiger-lily was the tallest, and red.

Sense and Nonsense . . . . page 106

Each vowel has been replaced with the following vowel alphabetically (and U with A). The decoded sentence reads: *Alice was beginning to get very tired of sitting by her sister on the bank, and of having nothing to do.*

Something Forgotten . . . . page 109

Her name.

Solutions

Nonsensical Numbers .... page 110
When you are adding clock times together.

Too Many Bishops .... page 114
Thirteen. There are fifteen diagonals on a chessboard going from top
left to bottom right, so there couldn't be more than fifteen bishops that didn't share a
diagonal (and in fact, you could not fit more than fourteen because the first and last
diagonal would share a perpendicular diagonal line). In addition, in a corner of the board
(where there is a diagonal of one that touches both squares of its adjacent diagonals of
two), there can only be one bishop in total in those two diagonals, otherwise they'd be
adjacent. This is true for both the top right corner and the bottom left corner (given that
we are considering diagonals from top left to bottom right), bringing the maximum down
to thirteen.

The Dinner Conundrum .... page 115
Alice, for the organizer of the tea had replaced "lice" with a synonym, "nits." The nameplate
could thus be read as "A lice," or "Alice."

More Sense and Nonsense .... page 116
Every other letter has been replaced with the previous letter alphabetically (and A with Z). The
decoded sentence reads: *One thing was certain, that the white kitten had had nothing to do
with it—it was the black kitten's fault entirely.*

Tweedledum and Tweedledee 6 .... page 118
Yes. The sentence *You may borrow the boat if and only if my name is Tweedledum* results
in the following possibilities:
a) Alice may borrow the boat and the speaker is Tweedledum; *or*
b) Alice may not borrow the boat and the speaker is not Tweedledum.
If the speaker was indeed Tweedledum, his sentence was true, so either a) or b) must be the
case. Moreover, as his name is Tweedledum, b) can't be true and so a) must be true, and
Alice may borrow the boat.
Alternatively, if the speaker was Tweedledee, his sentence was false, and neither a) nor b) is
true. Moreover, as his name is not Tweedledum, then it cannot be the case that Alice may
not borrow the boat, or else b) would be true. So, Alice may borrow the boat.

Solutions

Mathematical Mushroom 1 . . . . page 121

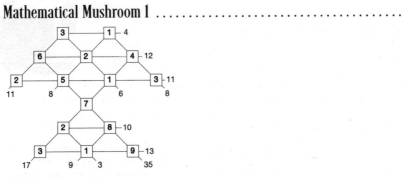

Back to Square One . . . . page 122

There are 204 squares: 64 that are 1×1, 49 that are 2×2, 36 that are 3×3, 25 that are 4×4, 16 that are 5×5, 9 that are 6×6, 4 that are 7×7, and one that is 8×8.

Broken Chessboard . . . . page 124

Chess and Dominoes . . . . page 128

No, it's not possible. Opposite corners of a chessboard are the same (both black or both white), so by cutting them off Tweedledee was left with either more black squares or more white squares. But each domino will cover exactly one white square and one black square, as no two white or black squares are adjacent. So after placing 30 dominoes, there will inevitably be two squares left, both either white or black. These will not be adjacent and so cannot be covered by a single domino.

Shifting Words 5 . . . . page 129

Shift each letter six places backward in the alphabet, so A becomes U, B becomes V, C becomes W, and so on, to read: *Down, down, down. Would the fall never come to an end?*

Solutions

Card Tricks .... page 130

The cards he gave to Alice were, apart from the three of diamonds, the only cards that are not rotationally symmetrical. If any of these had been rotated, he would have been able to see the rotation. But, because nothing had changed, he knew she must have rotated the only rotationally symmetrical card in the stack, the three of diamonds.

Card Watching .... page 133

42. There are four eyes on each of the four queen cards. There are four eyes on the kings of clubs, spades, and hearts, but the king of diamonds has only one eye on each face. There are four eyes on the jacks of diamonds and clubs, but the jacks of spades and hearts have only one eye on each face.

House of Cards .... page 134

9 layers. The bottom layer would have 10 cards in, then 4 flat cards, then 8 upright cards, then 3 flat cards, then 6 upright cards, then 2 flat, then 4 upright, then 1 flat, then 2 at the top, using 40 cards in total. This leaves only 12 cards, which is not enough for both a flat layer of 5 and an upright layer of 12 to be added beneath.

Blind Man's Bluff .... page 136

He sorted the cards into one pile of 16 and one pile of 36. He then flipped all the cards in the pile of 16.

Four of a Kind .... page 137

40. The answer is the same for one pack or for many. If you had 39 cards, you could have three of a kind of each value, but no four of a kind. The next card you drew would have to be the same value as one of the threes, making four of a kind.

Even More Sense and Nonsense .... page 140

Each letter has been swapped with its opposite in the alphabet, so A with Z, B with Y, C with X, and so on. The decoded passage reads: *Now, here, you see, it takes all the running you can do, to keep in the same place. If you want to get somewhere else, you must run at least twice as fast as that!*

Rebus 1 .... page 142

Six impossible things before breakfast: 6 × not "possible" before "things" before the broken "fast."

Solutions

Mad Multiplication . . . . page 143

Zero. Many (and at least one) of the residents of Wonderland do not have hands, and multiplying any number by zero gives zero as the answer.

Wonderland Zigzag 1 . . . . .page 145

C H E S H I R E
R E N E G A D E
D E C R E A S E
S E Q U O I A S
A S S A S S I N
I N N U E N D O
D O R M O U S E

Nonsense Pairs . . . . page 146

- Queen of Hearts
- Mad Hatter
- Alice
- March Hare
- Tweedledee

Letter Soup . . . . page 148

The names are Alice, Tweedledum, and Duchess.

Muddled Testimonies . . . . page 151

Bill the Lizard saw the Knave of Hearts sleeping in the Duchess' kitchen at 9 a.m. The White Rabbit saw him reading a book in the royal gardens at 2 p.m. The March Hare saw him eating the tarts beneath a giant mushroom at 7 p.m.

The Road to the Palace . . . . page 152

Only Alice: the others were all going in the opposite direction.

Solutions

The Giant Puppy .... page 154
Halfway. After that, you're leaving the woods again.

Rebus 2 .... page 159
Through the looking-glass: "LOOK" in "G-GLASS" through "THE."

A Slow Race .... page 160
She suggested that they swap trousers, or take a piece of each other's trousers. This would mean that whoever got there first could touch the other's trousers to the seat and thus win.

Lewis Carroll's Bookshelf .... page 162
Alice's Adventures in Wonderland was published in 1865 and is third from the top of the stack. *Through the Looking-Glass, and What Alice Found There* was published in 1871 and is at the top of the stack. *Phantasmagoria and Other Poems* was published in 1869 and is at the bottom of the stack. *The Hunting of the Snark* was published in 1876 and is second from the top of the stack.

Labyrinth 1 .... page 163   **Mathematical Mushroom 2** .. page 164

   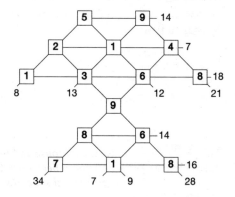

Guessing the Hand 1 .... page 165
He has (from left to right) a jack of diamonds, a queen of clubs, and a queen of diamonds.

Rebus 3 .... page 166
Alice in Wonderland: A "LICE" in "W" on "DERL" and an "and."

Solutions

From left to right, they should sit in the following order: Alice, the Hatter, the March Hare, the Dormouse, and then the White Rabbit.

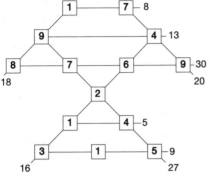

Down the rabbit hole: "THE" going down, and a hole in "RABBIT."

He has (from left to right) a two of hearts, a three of diamonds, a two of spades, and a seven of hearts.

The common word is *cat*. Each word on the list can be either preceded or followed by *cat* to make a dictionary entry: alley cat, cat burglar, fat cat, cat flap, house cat, and jungle cat.

The phrases are: mouse (*field mouse* and *mouse mat*), eagle (*spread eagle* and *eagle eye*), queen (*beauty queen* and *queen bee*), duck (*sitting duck* and *duck boat*), egg (*nest egg* and *egg timer*), and soup (*primordial soup* and *soup spoon*).

- The Caucus Race and a Long Tale
- The Queen's Croquet Ground
- The Rabbit Sends a Little Bill
- Who Stole the Tarts?

Solutions

LORY LORD FORD FOND FIND KIND KING
Five steps: LORY LORE LONE LINE KINE KING
Four steps: LORY LIRY LINY LING KING

- Alice's Evidence
- Pig and Pepper
- Down the Rabbit Hole
- The Pool of Tears

O	X	O	X	O	X	X	X
O	X	X	X	O	X	O	O
X	O	O	O	X	X	X	O
X	O	X	O	X	O	O	O
X	O	O	O	X	X	O	X
O	X	O	X	O	X	O	X
O	X	O	X	X	O	X	X
O	X	X	X	O	X	X	O

She need only take a maximum of ten sips. She could do this by putting a drop from each of 500 of the bottles in a glass and taking a sip. If this had an effect, she could discard the other 500. If not, she could discard the 500 that the sip had come from. She could then do the same by combining 250 bottles from the 500 she had left, and so on with 125 bottles, 63 bottles, 32 bottles, 16 bottles, 8 bottles, 4 bottles, 2 bottles and finally 1 bottle. When she drank that final bottle, if it had an effect, she would have found her potion—and if not, it was the other remaining bottle. This makes a total of 10 sips to identify the exact bottle.

The poem with the missing words reinserted is:

So rested he by the **Tumtum** tree
And the mome raths **outgrabe**
And **as** in uffish thought he stood
Did gyre and gimble in the wade

Solutions

Twas brillig, and the **slithy** toves
Came whiffling through the **tulgey** wood
One, two! **One**, two! And through and through!
O frabjous day! Callooh! Callay!
Long time the manxome foe he sought

So the word the first letters spell out is TOADSTOOL.

Rearranging Humpty Dumpty . . . . page 190

The full poem is:
Humpty (A) Dumpty (B) sat (C) on (D) a (E) wall (F)
Humpty (G) Dumpty (H) had (I) a (J) great (K) fall (L)
All (M) the (N) king's (O) horses (P) and (Q) all (R) the (S) king's (T) men (U)
Couldn't (V) put (W) Humpty (X) together (Y) again (Z)
The decoded quotation is therefore: *When I use a word it means just what I choose it to mean.*

Chessboard Assembly 1 . . . . page 193

B5	C3	A4	E2	D1
A1	D2	E5	C4	B3
D4	E1	B2	A3	C5
E3	B4	C1	D5	A2
C2	A5	D3	B1	E4

Word Changer 2 . . . . page 194

LION LIMN LIME LIRE HIRE HARE

Labyrinth 2 . . . . page 196

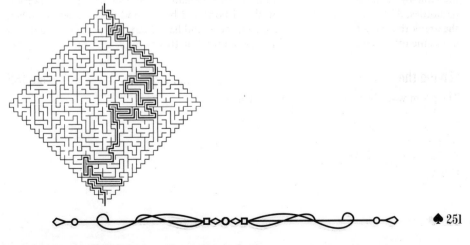

Solutions

Days and Days .... page 198

Monday.

Eating at the Tea-Party .... page 199

The Hare.

Alternate Letters 1 .... page 200

QUEEN OF HEARTS
CHESHIRE CAT
MARCH HARE
TWEEDLEDEE

The Hole .... page 201

The volume of soil inside the hole is clearly zero, or otherwise it would not be such a perfectly cut hole.

Attacking Knights 1 .... page 204

E	C	D	F	B	A
A	B	F	E	C	D
B	F	E	A	D	C
F	E	C	D	A	B
D	A	B	C	F	E
C	D	A	B	E	F

Wonderland Zigzag 2 .... page 206

NONSENSE
SEQUENCE
CEREBRAL
ALLERGEN
ENSHRINE
NEUTRINO
NONSENSE

Solutions

280 minutes. The White Rabbit was progressing at a rate of 2 m every ten minutes, so at the end of 270 minutes, he would have climbed 54 m. Therefore, at the end of the next ten minutes he would have reached the top by climbing the remaining 6 m, and it wouldn't matter that he would have slipped back down 4 m if he was still mid-climb.

WHITE RABBIT
MOCK TURTLE
TWEEDLEDUM
HUMPTY DUMPTY

Caterpillar: cat + er + pillar.

O	O	O	X	X	O	O	O
X	O	X	X	X	O	X	O
O	X	O	O	O	X	O	X
O	O	X	X	X	O	O	X
X	X	X	O	X	O	X	O
O	O	X	X	X	O	X	X
O	X	O	O	O	X	O	O
O	X	O	O	O	X	O	X

The rule will have no effect on the likelihood of any child being born a boy or a girl, no matter what other rules are applied. The only difference will be that some couples are forbidden from having further children.

One possible solution is ALICE SLICE SLICK STICK STOCK STORK STORY

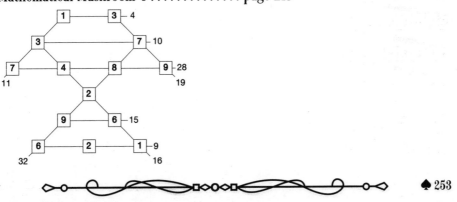

Solutions

One possible solution is SHEEP CHEEP CHEEK CHECK CHOCK CLOCK FLOCK

The Carpenter: car + pen + (tear − a).

C	G	B	D	F	A	E
D	B	G	F	C	E	A
A	E	F	C	B	G	D
E	F	D	A	G	B	C
F	D	A	G	E	C	B
B	A	C	E	D	F	G
G	C	E	B	A	D	F

Solutions

One possible solution is HEART HEARS HEATS SEATS SLATS SLITS SUITS

Duchess: (Duck-ck) + chess

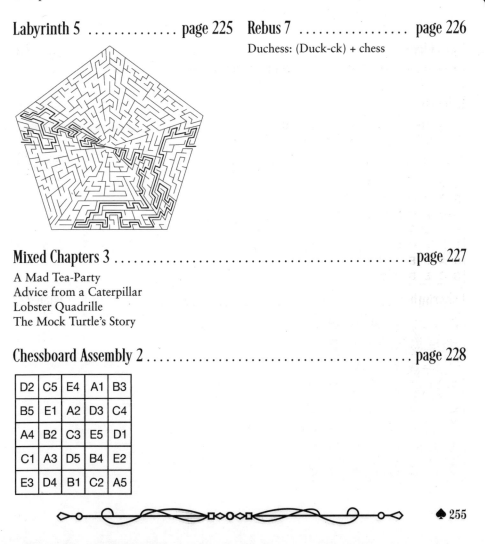

D2	C5	E4	A1	B3
B5	E1	A2	D3	C4
A4	B2	C3	E5	D1
C1	A3	D5	B4	E2
E3	D4	B1	C2	A5

Solutions

O	X	O	X	O	X	X	X
O	X	X	X	O	O	X	O
O	O	O	X	X	X	O	O
X	O	X	O	O	O	X	X
O	X	O	O	X	X	O	O
O	X	O	X	X	X	O	X
X	X	O	O	O	X	O	O
O	O	X	O	O	O	X	X

D1	C5	B2	A4	E3
C2	E4	A5	D3	B1
E5	B3	D4	C1	A2
A3	D2	E1	B5	C4
B4	A1	C3	E2	D5

Cheshire Cat: (chess − s) + h + (fire − f) + cat

B	F	E	D	A	G	H	C
H	G	C	E	D	A	B	F
G	H	A	B	E	C	F	D
F	D	B	A	G	E	C	H
E	C	D	F	H	B	A	G
C	E	F	H	B	D	G	A
A	B	H	G	C	F	D	E
D	A	G	C	F	H	E	B

Bury St Edmunds is a town whose history is rich in incidents and personalities. There is a story round every corner if we know where to look. Who was Jankyn Smyth and what was his great gift to the town? Where was the Widow's Coffee-House, and who was the Widow? Who had his nose slit in the Great Churchyard? When did the Great Flood take place? Who was Mr Bury? What was 'the beautiful light'? In *Bury St Edmunds: Historic Town* Elsie McCutcheon answers these questions and many more. Although this book is not a formal history, neither is it an uncritical repetition of local legends and anecdotes, as many 'popular' local histories tend to be. Wherever possible, the author has investigated the truth behind each story, using a wide variety of sources, including contemporary newspapers and local records such as Land Tax lists, parish registers and Census Returns. The end product is a book which will interest anyone – visitor or resident – who wants to know more about this venerable and picturesque town.

BURY ST EDMUNDS
HISTORIC TOWN

St Peter's Church

BURY ST EDMUNDS

HISTORIC TOWN

———————

Elsie McCutcheon

Drawings by Roma Bonney

Alastair Press
Suffolk

Published by
Alastair Press
2 Hatter Street
Bury St Edmunds
Suffolk

First published in 1987

© Text Elsie McCutcheon 1987
© Drawings Roma Bonney 1987

ISBN 1 870567 00 5

Typeset in 11/13½ Times by
Rowland Phototypesetting Ltd
Bury St Edmunds, Suffolk

Printed in England by
St Edmundsbury Press
Bury St Edmunds, Suffolk

Cover illustrations by J. C. Smith, 'The Autumn Fair at Bury St Edmunds
1808' by kind permission of the Clock Museum, Bury St Edmunds.

To Ken Wright and Alistair Robertson,
with thanks.

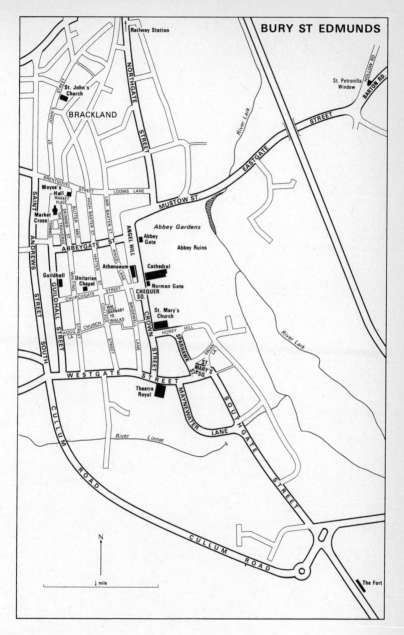

BURY ST EDMUNDS

Railway Station

St. John's Church

BRACKLAND

St. Petronilla Window

NORTHGATE STREET

HOLLOW RD.

BARTON RD.

STREET

EASTGATE STREET

River Lark

BRENTGOVEL STREET

Moyse's Hall

LOOMS LANE

MUSTOW ST.

Market Place

SAINT ANDREWS STREET

Market Cross

BUTTER MKT.

SKINNER ST.

THE TRAVERSE

HIGH BAXTER ST.

WM. BAXTER ST.

ABBEYGATE ST.

Abbey Gardens

Abbey Gate

ANGEL HILL

Abbey Ruins

Guildhall

Athenaeum

ANGEL LANE

Cathedral

HATTER ST.

Unitarian Chapel

WHITING STREET

Norman Gate

CHURCHGATE STREET

CHEQUER SQ.

St. Mary's Church

GUILDHALL STREET

HOGG LA.

CHURCH STREET

COLLEGE STREET

WM. BARNABY YD.

WALKS

BRIDEWELL LANE

CROWN STREET

HONEY HILL

SPARHAWK

SWAN LA.

River Lark

SOUTH STREET

WESTGATE STREET

ST. MARY'S SQ.

Theatre Royal

MAYNEWATER LANE

SOUTHGATE STREET

CULLUM ROAD

River Linnet

N

½ mile

CULLUM ROAD

The Fort

9

CONTENTS

LIST OF ILLUSTRATIONS

FOREWORD

The idea for this book was really conceived in Norfolk. It was while I was living there that I was persuaded by Chris Barringer to join a Local History Certificate Course, run by Cambridge University Extra-Mural Board. During the three years of that course I began to see that I could utilise my new-found skills in my part-time profession of freelance journalist. I decided that, one day, I might even write a book on some aspect of local history. With this aim in mind, I embarked on a detailed study of a Norfolk workhouse, a project which was never to come to fruition, since, in 1978, my husband accepted a post which was based in Bury St Edmunds. A disgruntled immigrant, still hankering after my workhouse, I was speedily consoled. Bury St Edmunds, I discovered, was a veritable cornucopia for a writer-cum-local historian. Soon I was spending much of my time in the local Record Office, unearthing the raw material of numerous articles for newspapers and magazines. Nine years later, *Bury St Edmunds: Historic Town*, is the result of my labours.

Many people have helped me, directly and indirectly in my research. I would like to thank the staff, (past and present), of Bury St Edmunds Record Office for their assistance and kindness. In particular Ken Wright and Alistair Robertson were ever helpful, encouraging, and enthusiastic, no matter how esoteric my requests, for which reason this book has been dedicated to them. Mrs Margaret Statham, too, (acknowledged to be our chief resident authority on Bury's history,) has allowed me, with unfailing good nature to intrude on her busy retirement with my inquiries. Friends have been equally supportive. Dr Pat Murrell generously put her extensive local collection at my disposal as well as offering helpful suggestions. Peter Northeast and David Dymond have patiently answered many a query over a pot of tea. Alison du Sautoy has read and made useful comments on the text, as well as compiling the index for me.

I am grateful to Roma Bonney for her patience and skill in producing the drawings. I would also like to thank the following for permission to reproduce photographs: Geoff Cordy, (pp.88 and 115) Mr O. G. Jarman, (p.27) and the Suffolk Record Office (p.63)

Finally, I must as always express my gratitude to my uncomplaining family, without whose co-operation this book could not have been written.

Elsie McCutcheon
May 1987

BURY ST EDMUNDS
HISTORIC TOWN

ROYAL VISITORS

Perhaps we in Bury may be forgiven if we preen ourselves occasionally on the town's illustrious past. In medieval times, particularly, the crowned heads of England came often to bow before the 'Shrine of a King'. Edward the Confessor was a frequent visitor, normally travelling the last mile of his pilgrimage on foot to show his devotion to the Saint. Henry II was crowned here. Richard the Lionheart paid his respects, both before setting out on the Crusade and after his return. On King John's first visit in 1199 the monks, according to Jocelin de Brakelond, believed 'he was come to make offering of some great matter; but all he offered was one silken cloth, which his servants had borrowed from our sacrist, and to this day have not paid for'. He returned in 1203, when he did make valuable offerings to the Shrine, but with the other hand took back all the rich jewels that his mother, Queen Eleanor, had presented to the Saint. It was following on his last visit in 1214, that the Barons assembled at the High Altar and swore to compel this little-loved king to grant Magna Carta.

Successive monarchs held parliaments in Bury, or came to pay protracted visits to the Abbey, as did the twelve-year-old Henry VI on Christmas Eve, 1433. Just what preparation this visit entailed is recorded in detail in the Register of the Abbot Curteys. The king announced his intention of coming to Bury on All Saints' Day, a wise precaution apparently, as, thereupon, eighty workmen had to be employed for a month to fit up the Abbot's palace, 'then in a state of decay and ruin.' A hundred officials, precursors of the royal party, had to be lodged and entertained, and there were consultations with the Aldermen and the Corporation about how they should dress to receive the king. It was eventually agreed that the Aldermen should wear scarlet and their inferiors red cloth gowns with blood-coloured hoods. Thus attired, a mile-long retinue of five hundred horsemen met the king on Christmas Eve at Newmarket Heath and escorted him back to the monastery. They were unable to enter by the main gateway as the way was blocked by the ruins of the Abbey's West Tower, which had collapsed two years previously, so the welcoming ceremony was performed in the street between the gate and the south door of the monastery. The Earl of Warwick lifted the boy-king from his horse, and, in front of the richly-attired monks, the Abbot, and the Bishop of Norwich, Henry knelt on a silk cloth, was sprinkled with holy water, and then given the crucifix to kiss. The procession then moved off to the High Altar, with the choir singing and the organs playing 'Ave Rex Gentis Anglorum' and after praying at the Shrine of St Edmund, Henry politely thanked the Abbot for his kindness and retired to the palace. He held a High Court during dinner on Christmas Day after High Mass, and thereafter celebrated the season of goodwill with fitting festivities, receiving handsome presents from the Abbot and Convent, both for himself and his nobles. Until Epiphany the young king lodged in the Prior's apartments, enjoying the salubrious air, (for which Bury has been renowned through the centuries) and the fragrance of the great vineyard, from the door of which he rode out to hunt the fox and the hare across the level fields and through the wooded groves. There was an interlude of fishing and hawking at Elmswell before Henry returned to the palace to keep Lent. Before his departure the boy was, at his own request, received into the brotherhood of the monastery.

It is interesting to compare Henry VI's winter visit to Bury with that of a twentieth-century monarch and his queen. In December, 1904, King Edward VII and Queen Alexandra,

20

who had been entertained at Culford Hall for five days, agreed to make a formal visit to Bury before leaving the area. This was the first visit a reigning sovereign had made to the town since Charles II passed through in 1668, and the borough was determined to celebrate it in style. By the morning of Saturday, December 17th, almost every street and building was bedecked with flags and bunting. The Abbey Gateway, one of the focal points of the tour, flew an East Anglian flag and a Union Jack, and on either side decorated grandstands had been erected to accommodate a thousand spectators. At ten a.m. an escort of the Duke of York's Own Loyal Suffolk Hussars, resplendent in green uniforms with red facings and yellow braid, set out to wait on Their Majesties at Culford Hall. The procession started for Bury just after noon, the King and Queen in a postillion barouche with two outriders carrying long whips, and the rest of the party following in two landaus. They entered the town in bright sunshine, making their way along Fornham Road and Northgate Street, and arriving in front of the Abbey Gateway at quarter-to-one.

Like all great institutions the Benedictine Abbey of St Edmunds had its vicissitudes. When Henry VI announced his forthcoming visit in 1433, Abbot Curteys's Palace, (the central building in the range at the rear of the Courtyard) was found to be in embarrassing disrepair. Perhaps this was why Henry later moved to the Prior's House, behind the Palace.

21

Angel Hill was thronged by this time with an immense, cheering crowd, some spectators having clambered on to the roofs of the Athenaeum and the Angel Hotel in order to obtain a better view. Just opposite the Gateway was the scarlet-coated band of the Third Battalion Suffolk Regiment, which had been playing to entertain the crowd prior to Their Majesties' arrival. The King received a loyal address from the Mayor and the Queen a bouquet from the Mayor's pretty daughter. A few presentations were made after which the party moved off through the Churchyard to St Mary's Church. The Vicar conducted the royal couple round the building, King Edward showing a particular interest in the tomb of Mary Tudor, sister of Henry VIII and Queen of France, and in her memorial window which had been presented by Queen Victoria in 1881. As the party finally left the church, they were greeted by the voices of two thousand assembled schoolchildren singing the National Anthem, and then breaking into three lusty cheers. As the cheers died away the bells of St Mary's and of the neighbouring St James's began to ring out, and continued to do so as the royal carriage made its way through the town to Northgate Station. The sun was still shining as the royal train steamed away towards London, leaving the flags gaily fluttering, the bands playing and the townsfolk in holiday mood.

King Edward VII and Queen Alexandra visited Bury on December 17, 1904. After receiving an address from the Mayor, they were conducted round St Mary's Church. As they left, the bells of the two parish churches rang out, and a choir of schoolchildren sang the National Anthem.

FAIR DAYS

The Town always seems to me a little dozy in the autumn, as though it's recuperating from the summer bustle. Most of the visitors have gone. The children are back in school. The whole tempo of the place has slowed. An ironic turn of events this, when one considers that for at least six centuries these weeks were the busiest and most important of the year for Bury's citizens. For it was in late September and early October that St Matthew's Fair was held. Such a notable fair, that the town teemed with visitors from all parts of England.

In 1272 Henry the Third granted the Abbot of Bury a charter for a fair to be held annually outside the monastery precincts. It was to be under the Abbey's sole jurisdiction, and from it the Abbot would reap lucrative tolls. Gillingswater, in his history of the town, conjures up a lively picture of this medieval fair, located (as it was until its demise), on Angel Hill, with the manufacturers of the various towns and cities such as London, Norwich, Ipswich, and Colchester, exhibiting their wares in separate rows of booths. It was primarily a trades-fair and it attracted Continental manufacturers, particularly the Dutch. In addition to the commercial transactions, there was a lighter side. There were jugglers and minstrels, acrobats and sweetmeat-sellers and a general atmosphere of revelry.

By the 16th century, the St Matthew's Fair was apparently attracting that elevated society for which it was to become renowned in the 17th and 18th centuries. For Mary Tudor, sister to Henry VIII and wife of the Duke of Suffolk, came from her manor of Westhorpe every year and had her own

23

luxurious pavilion erected on Angel Hill, where she entertained a bevy of noble guests and held court.

According to Daniel Defoe's sly insinuations, by 1724 Bury Fair had become primarily a marriage-mart for the gentry, and worse than that, perhaps. For, of the Assemblies in Fair-time, he declares, 'I venture to say that they are not the worst of the ladies who stay away . . . and I do not doubt but that the scandalous liberty some take at those Assemblies will in time bring them out of credit with the virtuous part of the sex here.' On the other hand, in 1750, a visitor to the town could write in the 'Gentleman's Magazine', 'The fair seems to be very justly termed the politest in the kingdom for the company that frequents it. The Duke of Grafton, Lord Cornwallis, Lord Hervey, are the constant ornaments . . . besides an innumerable concourse of knights and esquires with their wives and daughters from Norfolk, and Cambridge and all parts of Suffolk.'

From the mid-18th century we can follow the vicissitudes of the fair in local newspapers, particularly in the advertisement columns. Purveyors of fashionable attire flocked in from London, when Bury Fair was at its zenith, and there was a variety of entertainment. For example, in 1743, Rayner's Celebrated Company from Sadler's Wells proffered rope-dancing, tumbling, balancing, postures, singing and dancing in the Great Booth on Angel Hill, where there were side-boxes for 'the Quality'. In 1784, an exhibition next door to Anderson's Coffee-House, included, for a shilling, Mr Jervais's collection of pictures in stained glass and Mr Deane's transparent paintings, which depicted, by reflections in a vast concave mirror, the conflagration in London during the 1780 riots, and 'Mount Vesuvious' in various stages of eruption! In this year, too, Mr O'Burne, the eight-foot tall Irish Giant was to be seen in his caravan on Angel Hill. Romance could blossom and matches be made at the elaborate evening balls, or at the morning 'Ordinaries' in the Angel Inn. Theatre-audiences could enjoy a wide range of drama, from Shakespeare to the latest trivial farce.

In 1825 Madame Tussaud brought her collection to the Concert Room, (the present Market Cross), where it rapidly seems to have become the fair's chief attraction. It was advertised as 'a splendid promenade with magnificent Coronation groups', and in the evening visitors could enjoy it to the music of a military band. All the most noble families visited it, and parents were exhorted to take their children for educational purposes.

Ten years later, one of the Fair's highlights was a balloon ascent by the intrepid Mr Green, who had 209 ascents to his credit already. On this occasion he was accompanied by a Mr Gocher of Bury and Mr Crawshay, junior, of Honingham Hall. They took to the air at three o'clock on a Friday afternoon from Bury Cattle Market and at four-twenty descended safely in Hoxne, whence they were carried off to a 'sumptuous tea' by the Reverend Richard Cobbold of Wortham, before being transported triumphantly back to Bury in a chaise-and-four.

But the story of Bury Fair is by no means one of unmarred jollity and goodwill. The local shopkeepers in particular did not alway view the ancient institution with favour and from time to time efforts were made to curtail it. As early as 1734 a notice appeared in the 'Ipswich Journal' to the effect that 'St Matthew's Fair, which . . . hath of late years been prolonged and continued from the 18th day of September till the 8th or 9th of October, and sometimes longer . . . for the future will not be continued longer than the 2nd day of October . . . and all persons selling goods or wares therein . . . after that time, will be prosecuted.' But it was in 1815 that real bitterness arose between the visiting traders and the local fraternity, as a result of which legal proceedings were taken and the 'Bury Fair Case' became news.

By this period the Fair was generally known as Bury

Michaelmas Fair and its duration was normally extended until the end of October. According to the evidence given in the 1815 court case, the Fair was traditionally held three days before, and three days after the Feast of St Matthew, September 21. It was then publicly proclaimed open by the Alderman on September 29 for the ensuing three weeks. At the end of that period it was the custom for the fair-traders to apply for, and be granted, an extension until the last market day in October.

In 1815, however, one John Biers of Middlesex, described as a 'common informer, who goes about the country to lay informations against any breaking the law', was invited to come to Bury by some of its shopkeepers. It is probable that his daughter was also his accomplice, for it emerged that she had one of the booths at the Fair that year. On October 26 the traders had made their customary application to the Alderman for an extension until the 28th of the month, and it had been granted. On Friday October 27, however, John Biers accused two traders of infringing the Hawkers and Pedlars Act, by selling without a licence. The two were Joseph Gedge of Norwich, who sold glass and plates, and Sarah Green of London, who was selling soap and starch. Both traders declared that they were selling legally within the Fair, to which Biers retorted that only the initial six days of the Fair were legal fair days. When Biers laid his information before the Alderman, (himself a Bury shopkeeper), the accused were taken before the magistrates, found guilty and fined the not inconsiderable sum of £10 each.

Understandably the Fair-traders were infuriated at this judgement. They decided to appeal against it, using the services of a Bury solicitor, Frederick Wing. Mr Wing fought a skilful and triumphant battle on their behalf. He emphasised, first of all, that Mr Gedge and Mrs Green were most respectable tradespeople, who could in no wise be considered hawkers or pedlars. He showed that Biers was a doubtful character, and had in fact offered to drop one of the charges, on condition that one of the £10 fines was paid. He pointed out that the Bailiff's Booth, (formerly the Pie Powdre Court) was still open and selling beer on October 27, which was irrefutable evidence of the legal continuance of the Fair. He finished by declaring that if the convictions were confirmed, Bury Fair, 'that genteel respectable mart', to which nobility and gentry came yearly from distant parts of the kingdom, 'for polite and friendly intercourse' would vanish. And all through the greed and malice of the Bury shopkeepers.

The traders won their battle in 1815. But by 1825 there were signs that the Michaelmas Fair was starting on a slow decline. According to the 'Bury and Norwich Post' in October that year, the duration of the fair had lately been much curtailed, with the short season beginning much later than had previously been the case. On October 12, for example, 'from time immemorial claimed by the rustics as their own',

From the Middle Ages to the 19th century merchants and members of the gentry flocked to Bury for its renowned autumn Fair. Henry III's tailor was despatched to Bury Fair to buy his master black and scarlet robes, trimmed with fur. By the 18th century the Fair had the reputation of being a marriage mart for the aristocracy.

there hadn't been a single attraction apart from the booths and the public houses. No 'procession of the riders'. No 'band of the wild beasts'. No 'Merry Andrew' or 'Punchinello' . . . A sad disappointment for the country folk who had trudged into Bury from miles around, dressed in their 'Sunday best'.

Surprisingly, though, the Fair staggered on for almost another fifty years, with increasing complaints about it from the townsfolk. By 1866 it was a notorious bone of contention in Bury, and its duration had been limited to a fortnight. By this stage, entertainment was its primary function, and it was catering for the masses and not for the gentry. As described in the 'Bury Free Press' of October 2, 1866, it was composed of 'two rows of confectionery and toy stalls, boarded in, with just space enough to walk down between them, and at the northern end of the hill, High's and Barker's steam hippodromes, a representation of the old-fashioned merry go rounds, swinging boats, and rifle and pistol ranges'. There were also three photographic studios, a peep-show, and sausage-booths. It was in this year that a petition was raised for the Fair's abolition on the grounds of 'immorality', and the nuisance it caused to the residents on Angel Hill. Ironically this petition was signed by all those rural gentry, for whom, and around whom, Bury Fair had once revolved. It was another five years before the kill-joys had their way and the Michaelmas Fair finally died, leaving the town to sleep, as it does today, in the mellow sunshine, and to dream of all those colourful and lively autumns in its past.

JANKYN'S GIFT

If you walk along Bridewell Lane, you will pass the attractive little building that is the Guildhall Feoffment School. If you wander into St Mary's Church and look in the Lady Chapel in the south chancel aisle, you will see two brasses commemorating Jankyn Smyth and his wife. What is the connection?

John, or Jankyn, Smyth lived in Bury St Edmunds in the fifteenth century. We know certain important facts about him. He was the son of John and Hawise Smyth. He was almost certainly a wealthy merchant. His wife's name was Anne, and he had at least two children, John, and Rose. Rose's husband was to be appointed supervisor of Jankyn's will, and her children were to receive generous bequests.

As regards Jankyn's public life, he was elected Alderman, the equivalent of our Mayor, no less than seven times between 1423 and 1481. We know that on one occasion the Abbot refused to confirm his election. It has been deduced from this, that, since Jankyn was a member of the powerful Candlemas Guild, he was regarded by the Abbey as being too ambitious, and hence dangerous.

We can make some educated guesses about other aspects of Smyth's life. According to the Sacrist's Rental of 1433, he owned a house in Churchgate Street, between Hatter Street and Angel Lane, so it seems likely that he lived there. He seemed to fear that his son, John, might try to alter the bequests in his will, so we can deduce that he did not have a totally satisfactory relationship with him.

The Candlemas Guild, which catered for the business, social, and religious interests of its members, must have played a major part in their lives. It met in the Guildhall, that marvellous building we can visit today in Guildhall Street. The members of the Guild were responsible for the upkeep of the buildings. It is thought that Jankyn Smyth played a part in planning the extensive alterations to the building which took place in the latter part of the fifteenth century; he still looks down from the wall of the Banqueting Chamber, a dark-haired, bearded, shrewd-looking man, wearing a black gown, and holding a book and a pair of gloves. However, it was after Jankyn's death that he really made his mark on the town. In his will he left two hundred and thirty-eight acres of land to Feoffees, all brother members of the Candlemas Guild. The revenues from this land were to be used not only to provide annual memorial services for the souls of himself and dead relatives, but also for the general benefit of the townspeople, mainly by assisting them in the payment of burdensome taxes. What Jankyn Smyth had done in effect, was found the Guildhall Feoffment Charity which has played a notable part in Bury St Edmunds' history throughout the centuries.

Smyth was the leader of what was to be a long line of benefactors, whose concern for their fellow-citizens took the form of bequests to the Guildhall Feoffment Trust. These have included money, or land, to provide poor-relief, alms-houses, medical treatment, fuel and food for prisoners, stipends for the curates of the two churches, and educational services. Some benefactors left buildings. William Tassell, for example. In 1556 he left the Trust the 'Angel', and an adjacent inn as well. And in 1579 Thomas Badby bequeathed the building which had been the grammar school of the monastery, for use as a Shire House. In our own day, Mrs E. P. Greene, Mayor from 1932–3, and the first woman to have become a Feofee, left money which has been used to plant ground at the entrance to the almshouses known as Jankyn's Place.

Through the centuries the Trust has worked for the benefit

and happiness of the townspeople. Happiness implied order. The rules, drawn up in 1582 for the inhabitants of the alms-houses, exhorted them to live, 'in peace and quietness, without brawling, drunkenness, or idleness.'

In 1587, during an epidemic of plague, the infected residents were moved into tents in the fields round the town. The Guildhall Feoffees gave ten pounds and three shillings 'towards the charges of the keepers and bearers, and in the reliefe of the pore beings visited with sikenes, five shillings to Joseph Nunne for a loode of poules bought of hym and imploied about the making of tents for th'infected.'

After 1606 the Trust worked hand-in-hand with the newly-formed Corporation. That it sometimes took on the duties of

The porch of the building is early Tudor, but inside there is a stone doorway dating from the 13th century. The front, (apart from the porch) was refaced at the beginning of the 19th century. The Guildhall was used for many years for Petty Sessions, and the Town Council met here until 1966.

a 'Highway Committee' can be seen in an entry in the Minutes for 1662:

'Whereas the Angel Hill is much in decay and great heaps of muck are there laid to the annoyance of the place and the discord of the Town, and whereas the Corporation is at present not in good condition to repair the same by reason of some extraordinary charges they have been at, the Feoffees have voluntarily agreed to repair the same by laying many loads of gravell upon the same, and setting up gutters, and to cause the muck to be carried away . . .'

The Feoffees granted pensions to deserving cases. In 1676 it was decided, 'That Mr Receiver give to Benjamin Major five shillings at present; and that if he be a good husband and the Feoffees hear well of him, then the next Receiver shall give him five shillings more after Lady Day.'

They provided fuel and food for prisoners. In 1698 it was agreed that, since the old Town Gaol had been replaced by two gaols, one for the town and one for the county, the fuel formerly allowed to the prisoners should be divided into two equal portions to serve each new gaol.

By the beginning of the century, the Trust owned three schools – a girls' school in Short Brackland, a boys' school, and a Commercial School. The two latter were in the Bridewell Lane–College Street area. In 1931 they were extended, and amalgamated to become a Provided Council School which was opened with much ceremony on September 3, 1932. The school is still known as the Guildhall Feoffment School and it receives a small financial contribution from the Trust.

Nowadays when the name of the Guildhall Feoffment Trust crops up, it is usually in connection with its three sets of almshouses – attractive, modernized homes for the elderly in College Square, Southgate Street, and Chalk Road. Though of course it still makes frequent generous contributions to local 'good causes', such as the hydrotherapy pool, bought for the West Suffolk Hospital a few years ago.

Jankyn Smyth died on June 28, 1481. His Commemoration Service is now held annually on the Thursday before the 29th of June, St Peter's Day. It takes place in the beautiful church of St Mary's, the building of whose chancel aisles he paid for in his lifetime, and the repair of which he provided for, with money and land, in his bequest. The Sanctuary too was probably paid for out of Smyth's money. A notable man in his day, he used his wealth to buy for himself an enviable immortality.

According to White's 1844 *Directory*, the Commercial School in College Street afforded instruction 'to 150 boys in English and other living languages, in writing, arithmetic, geography, history, and so much of the mathematics and dead languages as may be practicable or useful.'

FURIOUS FIRE

Like most towns, Bury has been ravaged by fire at various times in its history. One of the most devastating conflagrations was in 1608, and because a contemporary pamphlet was printed about it, we know the salient details. Headed, 'The Woefull and Lamentable Waste and Spoile done by suddaine Fire in St Edmonsburie in Suffolk on Munday the tenth of Aprill, 1608,' this pamphlet uncharitably describes the calamity as a divine retribution for the 'secret sins and offences' of the townsfolk.

The fire began, it appears, between eight a.m. and nine a.m. in Eastgate Street, outside the town gate, in the house of one Randall, a maltster, and was the result of 'a remiss and sleepy negligence of a servant'. Although it started about half-a-mile from the market-place, a strong wind soon carried it in that direction, where it did immense damage. The market-place, described as 'the beautie and ornament of the whole towne', and much admired for its houses and stately buildings, was soon reduced to 'a rude continent of heapes of stones and peeces of Timber,' The warehouses and cellars that had been stocked with fish, salt, sugar, spices, and other valuable commodities were entirely consumed and their owners left in dire poverty and misery. Walls, hedges, and fences, were burned to the ground. Mr Pinner, a grocer of St James's Parish had to watch his newly-built house, which had cost him between four and five hundred pounds, devoured by the flames, and all his stock, goods and plate with it. Mr Cox, a draper, also lost everything, apart from a little yarn he had stored in a warehouse in another place. The Market Cross was burned to the ground and its lead melted by the intense heat.

The fire raged from Monday until Wednesday, defying all efforts to control it, although all the wells and ponds in the vicinity were drawn dry. In the end it was calculated that it had destroyed over two hundred houses, countless barns full of unthreshed corn, and thousands of quarters of threshed wheat, barley and rye stored in upper rooms. Livestock, too, such as horses, cattle and pigs perished in the flames, including two unfortunate horses that had just drawn a corn-laden cart into the market-place, when the fire broke out. In all, the damage of the great fire of 1608 was assessed at £100,000. We can see a form of memorial of the event today in the inscription on the front of the restaurant in the Buttermarket. This early 19th century plaque, which replaces the original one reads:

'Burgus ut antiquus violento corruit igne
Hic stet dum flammis terra polusque flagranto.'
This has been translated as:
'Tho' furious fire the old Town did consume
Stand this till all the world shall flaming fume.'

It is believed that the inscription, which originally had the date 1609 beneath it, was affixed to a new house built on the ruins of a burned one.

Another major fire in Bury's history occurred on the night of the 16th–17th June, 1882. Had it not been contained in time, it might well have destroyed a large area around Angel Hill. As it was, it destroyed a substantial block of property along Abbeygate Street and on the corner of Hatter Street. The premises in question were the large stationery and printing business, and the County Club on the corner, and in Abbeygate Street, a tobacconist's shop, a butcher's, a photographer's, a greengrocer's and a drapery store. In most cases the proprietors of these businesses lived above them, although in the old brick-faced stud-and-plaster houses, several upper chambers overlapped the ground floors of adjoining shops.

It was the butcher's wife who first became aware of the fire just before midnight. She had been sitting up waiting for her husband to come home, and heard what sounded like someone breaking into the shop. In the event this turned out to be, on further investigation, the crackling of the fire. The woman rushed out into the street with her children, screaming, 'Fire!' and 'Murder!' A young man, who was passing, ran down an alleyway to the back of the buildings to see where the blaze was. It was to be largely on this witness's evidence that the man who was eventually charged with arson was convicted. Meanwhile the County Club caretaker, who lived opposite the club, had been alerted; he ran down Abbeygate Street ringing doorbells to rouse his neighbours, while the alarm was taken along to the police-office and the firemen. The draper had a large household to evacuate for, as well as his family and servants, there were four assistants, and a clerical gentleman and his wife living there as lodgers. In common with most of the other shops, nothing was saved from the drapery except the books.

It was between twelve-thirty and twelve-forty-five before the firemen had their first hose working and by this time the fire had a formidable grip. It was thought at this stage to have originated either in the County Club or in the tobacconist's. By one a.m. the crowd that had gathered saw the fronts of the buildings fall out into Abbeygate Street. Two hours later the whole corner crashed down, blocking Hatter Street. The fear then was that the blaze would spread to the conglomeration of stables and wooden sheds at the rear of the burning properties, and start to eat its way southwards becoming virtually unstoppable. Fortunately, there was no wind. By skilful plying of their hoses on adjacent rooftops, the firemen eventually contained the blaze, and by five a.m. it was extinguished.

The first shock development after the fire was the arrest of the tobacconist on a charge of attempting to defraud an insurance company. A young man of thitherto unblemished character, his case was referred to the August Assizes. Here it emerged that he had been in great financial difficulties for some time, had just recently over-insured his business, and was currently making arrangements to buy another shop elsewhere. The evidence of one of his shop-boys was damning. He attested to the tobacconist's having severed, and nipped

THE

Woefull and Lamentable

wast and spoile done by a suddaine
Fire in S. Edmonds-bury in
Suffolke, on Munday, the tenth
of Aprill. 1608.

LONDON

Printed for Henrie Gosson, and are to be solde in Pater-
noster rowe, at the Signe of the Sunne.
1608

The Bury Fire of 1608. Fire was all too often an insuperable foe before the days of organised fire-fighting. Wooden houses and thatched roofs were ready-made pyres. Ladders, buckets of water, and long-handled hooks were ineffectual weapons. No wonder the victims turned to praying . . . or weeping.

together, a gas-pipe in the back part of the cellar before putting up a shelf above the pipe on which he stacked a quantity of cigar-boxes. This testimony, combined with that of the passer-by who had run to the back of the building when the fire was starting, was of prime importance. The latter witness swore that he had seen flames, such as would come from a fractured gas-pipe, leaping up behind the back window in the tobacconist's cellar. The tobacconist's defence was to suggest that the fire had been started by a careless pedestrian dropping a cigar-end or a lucifer through the grating of the cellar at the Abbeygate Street side. At the first trial the jury were unable to agree. The case was deferred until the next Assizes, when the tobacconist was finally found guilty and sentenced to five years' penal servitude.

There were many repercussions after the Great Fire of 1882. The debate on whether the town ought to have a fire-escape was resurrected again. There was much criticism of the tardiness of the firemen in getting their hoses working. There was a proposal to set up reels with hose at other points in the town, apart from the police-station. Finally there was the decision to take this opportunity of widening Abbeygate Street at the point of rebuilding, by pushing back the new frontings by two feet. Once again the face of Bury had been marked, albeit slightly, by the ravages of its ancient enemy – Fire.

> Burgus ut antiquus violento corruit igne
>
> Hic stet dum flammis terra polosque flagranto

This plaque is to be found on a building just to the west of Moyses Hall in the Buttermarket. Although it dates from the 19th century, the inscription that it bears is said to come from a much earlier plaque, on which was the date 1609. Apparently this had been affixed to one of the new buildings which rose from the ashes.

UNQUENCHABLE SPIRITS

If it is true, as some people believe, that places retain the spirit of whatever human dramas are enacted there, then I should not care to be working in those buildings, which at the time of writing, comprise the Job Centre and the Eastern Electricity shop on Cornhill. For it was somewhere here that Bury Gaol stood in 1655, when the gaoler, a ruthless man called Robert Newton, set out to break the spirits of a group of Quakers in his charge.

To many people the word Quaker is synonymous with pacifism, docility and demure staidness, but one has only to walk into a modern Meeting House and chat with these lively, practical Christians to be rid of these misconceptions. Even a brief look into the history of the Society shows that its founders could not have been a more dynamic or courageous group of people.

George Fox, as everyone knows, was the man whose vision founded the movement. A Leicestershire country lad, apprenticed to a shoemaker, he was still a teenager, when, bewildered and frustrated by the disrupted society and the religious ferment of the 1640s, he left home and took to the road in the search for a spiritual truth which would satisfy him. By the time he was twenty years old, he had found his answer in a return to a pure and primitive Christianity, which rejected all the accoutrements of organised religion. Priests and churches or 'steeple-houses', as he termed them, he saw as mere obstacles between the worshipper and Christ. Fox's Christianity was a living, and constantly growing faith, which made nonsense of the Puritan doctrine of Predestination. It was a faith which, in those troubled times, was bound to excite fear and enmity, as well as attracting a body of devoted followers.

George Fox recruited these followers mainly from Puritan sects like the Baptists of Mansfield, amongst whom he worked in 1648. In 1649 he was imprisoned for the first time in Nottingham because he had interrupted a sermon in the parish church. In 1650 he was arrested at Derby and imprisoned for a year under the Blasphemy Act. This was to be the pattern both for himself and his followers until the Toleration Act was passed in 1689.

These early Friends were persecuted on many counts. The charge of blasphemy was a popular one. Their refusal to pay tithes, or church rates, incensed the authorities and resulted in severe punishments. They deliberately flouted social conventions, denying that any one man was superior to another, and refusing to remove their hats, or to bow to 'gentlemen', or to the magistrates in court. They refused to swear any oaths at all, in obedience to Christ's command in the Sermon on the Mount. They were adept at making public nuisances of themselves, when they saw any blatant injustice or wrongdoing which needed to be righted.

In 1651 Fox moved north to Yorkshire and Westmoreland, and his subsequent contact with a congenial Puritan sect called the Seekers resulted in his first large influx of converts. These were the young, dynamic idealists, many of them in their teens and early twenties, who were to become the nucleus of the movement. By the end of 1653 the first missionaries were sent south. Early in 1654 sixty-six others followed them, amongst them Richard Hubberthorne and George Whitehead, who were sent to East Anglia. In July, 1655, George Whitehead, a nineteen year old schoolteacher from Westmoreland, was arrested with another friend, John Harwood, in Bures, and eventually sent up to Bury and thrown into the gaol, which as I have said, occupied a site near the corner of Woolhall Street and Cornhill.

In September these two were joined by the valiant George Rofe, a glazier from Halstead, who, earlier in the year, had almost been killed by an irate mob in Hythe. Rofe's 'crime' on this occasion was that he had asked a question of the minister of Stoke Nayland church at the end of his sermon. The three of them were taken up before the magistrates at the October Quarter Sessions in Bury and indicted as 'common disturbers of the Magistrates and Ministers'. Another Friend, who had witnessed this travesty of justice, protested to one of the Justices at the Sessions-House door, and was immediately arrested and imprisoned too. He was George Fox, the Younger, from Chasefield, no relative to the founder of the movement. In November Henry Marshall, a Cambridgeshire Friend, was arrested in Boxford for questioning a priest and sent up to Bury gaol. The imprisonment of these five Friends has resulted in light being shed on one of the more unsavoury aspects of Bury's history. For, as so many of their sect did, they wrote down in great detail the abuses which they had to suffer while in gaol and they published their complaints in a pamphlet, wordily entitled, 'The Grounds and Causes of our Sufferings related in short, who suffer by the Cruelty of OPPRESSORS in Edmonds-Bury Gaol in SUFFOLK.'

The chief oppressor was the gaoler, Robert Newton. The 'grounds and causes' of the Quakers' sufferings were basically pecuniary ones arising from Newton's greed. For to keep a gaol in 1655 was rather like keeping a horrendous boarding-house, with the inmates having to pay 'entry' and 'exit' fees, and various levels of rent according to the accommodation and the comfort they could afford. The 'common gaol' was free and intended for the penniless. Newton had obviously expected a group of educated and comparatively well-off men like the Quakers to pay well for their comforts. In this he was mistaken, for all of them asked to be housed in the common gaol where they had to pay only for the straw which was sent in for them to lie on.

Towards the end of 1655, Newton, maddened by the Quakers' persistent refusal to rent rooms and beds from him, began to use physical violence against them, punching them himself, and encouraging the gaol's tapster to do likewise. He also incited the other prisoners to attack them and stone them, plying them with drink to inflame them.

In the spring of 1656, when there was no sign of the Quakers being released, Newton changed his tactics. He marched into the common gaol on the 16th of April and demanded payment for their keep. When they asked how much he wanted, he told them fourteen pence a week, with George Whitehead and John Harwood owing thirty-one weeks of arrears. The Friends refused to pay for being housed in what was a free gaol, and the furious Newton ordered the turnkey to confiscate all their possessions. This included their nightclothes, the boxes in which they stored their linen and their food, and even their nightcaps, 'which hung in a basket by the wall'. When he threatened to take the clothes from their backs, the Quakers told him sarcastically to go ahead, since he had robbed them of everything else. For some reason he backed down and said he would wait until the warmer weather set in. He countered an accusation that he was a shame to his profession by telling the Quakers they were heretics and he could treat them as he wished.

Newton returned to the attack on the 28th of April. He first of all informed the Quakers that it was only through his 'courtesy' that they had been allowed to keep their clothes during the winter, for the magistrates had ordered they should be deprived of them. Then, when one of the Bury Quakers, a woman who had obviously heard of her comrades' plight, arrived at the gaol with two shirts, two caps, two bands and four handkerchiefs for them, Newton confiscated the clothes immediately, and, for good measure, had his turnkey tear off George Rofe's coat. Probably thinking that discomfort would weaken his victims, Newton came in again two days later to offer them new terms. He promised them that should they pay their rent-arrears of fourteen pence a week, he would return their possessions. When met with the usual refusal, and a demand to know by what right he was charging for free accommodation, he changed his tactics and he said that if they paid the arrears anyway, then rented rooms with beds from him at seven groats a week, they would be granted 'the privileges in the house.' This would mean a larger yard to walk in, access to Newton's own garden, and visits from their friends.

It must have been a tempting proposition for those five men, cooped up in what we know was a black, noisome, dungeon of a place, with a rabble of ruffians. However, they

The Friends' Meeting House, St. John's Street. In 1682 Bury Friends purchased, for fifty pounds, 'two low rooms . . . and one piece of ground' on this site in Brackland. In 1750 the old house was replaced by the present building, of timber frame, with a tall Venetian window in the centre of its east wall. The roof was re-tiled in 1962.

were determined that the gaoler should make no profit out of them, and once again they rejected his offers. Predictably Newton resorted as before to physical violence, using his own servants and the other prisoners as tools, with which to vent his spite. It was at the height of this persecution that the five wrote down their experiences and probably smuggled the paper out so that it could be printed as the pamphlet which we can read today.

The persecution of Friends continued, with peaks and troughs, until almost the end of the 17th century. Until 1682 Bury Quakers held their meetings in private houses, often suffering severely for so doing. Then in 1682 they bought a property in St John's Street for their permanent Meeting House. The charming building we can see today was built on this same site in 1751. On the morning that I visited it, the beautifully-tended little burial-ground was pulsating with birdsong after a shower of rain. Sunlight streamed in through the tall eastern window of the building. The happy sound of children's voices and laughter floated out from the entrance-hall, as the playgroup dispersed. It seemed a far, far journey from that terrible prison on Cornhill, where the story of Bury's Quakers had its unhappy beginnings.

POSTAL CHANGES

The public postal service is a surprisingly ancient institution. Indeed, when it started in the 1630s, the folk of Bury would doubtless be receiving news of outbreaks of plague or famine, perhaps of the burning of witches in their mail. Yet even in these remote times the system was well-organised.

In 1677 the Postmaster-General was the Lord Chamberlain, the Earl of Arlington. His Grand or General Office was in Bishopgate Street in London, where both incoming and outgoing domestic and foreign mail was dealt with. The mail for East Anglia was despatched on Tuesdays, Thursdays and Saturdays. This General Office was managed by a Deputy and seventy-seven other officers. There were 182 Deputy Postmasters in England and Scotland, most of whom kept regular offices. These members of staff and the twelve packet-boats used for Continental mail had to be maintained at the Postmaster's own expense. Nevertheless it was obviously a lucrative post, for it was farmed out for no less than £30,000 a year, in modern values several million pounds. If what was claimed for the service in 1677 was true, it was amazingly efficient. Letters were carried more cheaply than in other countries, the price of a one-sheet letter being twopence for eighty miles. The post was reckoned to travel 120 miles every twenty-four hours, and the reply to a letter travelling 300 miles could be expected within five days.

By the mid 18th Century the postboy was a familiar figure on our country's roads. These 'boys', of all ages, carried the Royal Mail on horseback along roads which would have been impossible for wheeled vehicles. Theirs was a hazardous life, as is evidenced in the following notice, issued by the General Post Office, and found in the 'Publick Intelligencer' for April 28, 1757:

'Whereas the post-boy bringing the Norwich mail from Epping to this office was this morning about four o'clock attacked and robbed on the road by the Obelisk and High Stone near Laytonstone, Essex, by a single highwayman on horseback who presented a pistol to the post-boy, at the same time ordering him to deliver him the Mail, otherwise he would blow his brains out, which obliged the post-boy to unstrap the mail and deliver it to the Highwayman, who took the whole Norwich Mail before him upon his horse and rode away with it full speed towards Epping.' Among the bags included in the Norwich Mail was the one for Bury St Edmunds. The Post Office offered £200 reward for the apprehension of the robber, in addition to the normal Government reward for the apprehension of a highwayman.

Before the introduction of letter-boxes one had to 'catch the bellman' who made his rounds with a large leather bag to receive mail, the postage being paid by the recipient. Wall letter-boxes were introduced in this country in the early 19th century, and pillar-boxes in the 1850s. In provincial towns the latter were usually green in colour until 1884, when the familiar bright red was adopted.

Mr W Dawson, the Bury St Edmunds Postmaster, who retired in 1893, granted an interview to the Press on that occasion in which he painted a valuable picture of the development of the postal service in the town during the second half of the 19th century.

Mr Dawson had arrived in Bury from Shrewsbury in 1861 to find that his new Post Office was a primitive affair. In fact it was part of a shop at Number 10, The Buttermarket and the public transacted their business from the street through a small window only a foot square. Not long after his arrival however, the office moved to Number 24, Abbeygate Street.

The progression to an indoor office was obviously an improvement, but these premises were still not large enough to accommodate an ever-increasing postal trade and the position of the Office, at the lower end of the street, was far from ideal for the parking of Post Office vehicles.

In 1881, therefore, there was another move to 52, Abbeygate Street, which had been the premises of Gurney's Bank. The Bank had moved into a new building next door whose facade had been designed to match that of Number 52. This move caused a lot of local discord. There was a body of opinion which favoured the Town Hall, now the Market Cross, as a home for a new Post Office. Another was equally as fervent in its claims for the Indoor Market in Cornhill. Indeed there was a proposal to send a deputation to the Postmaster-General, but this idea was nipped in the bud. Apparently the Government wanted no part of Bury's Town Hall or Market building. It had decided on Number 52, Abbeygate Street. So, despite prophecies of disaster by local Jonahs, who described that location as the most hazardous in the town, that was where the Post Office went.

The 1881 Post Office was the first sizeable one in Bury. The public office on the ground floor was twenty-seven feet wide and eighteen feet deep. There was a large detached sorting-office, which was connected to the main building by a covered way. The telegraph operations were carried out on the first floor. The second floor was used for stores and the basement was occupied by the caretaker. During the next fourteen years the business of Bury Post Office increased considerably, so much so that the sorting-office had to be extended in 1890. In his interview Mr Dawson quoted some impressive figures. When he started in Bury in 1861, he had had three clerks, two 'full' letter-carriers, and two extra hands for the morning delivery. By 1893 he had fifteen clerks, ten 'full' letter-carriers and four auxiliaries. The town deliveries had increased from two to five a day.

Two years after Mr Dawson's retirement the Post Office moved to its present location on Cornhill on part of the site of the demolished Bell Hotel. It was inevitable that the advantages of the Abbeygate Street building should immediately be discerned. It had been much more central and convenient and the Postmaster felt that his old room had been much superior to his gloomy new one. However, it had to be admitted that the front of the new building, brick with stone facings and with the Royal Arms carved on the top gable, did improve the appearance of Cornhill and business continued to boom.

The bustle of the Christmas rush at Bury Post Office in the early years of this century was described in the local Press in

Bury's Victorian Post Office. The external appearance of the Cornhill Post Office is little changed from when it was erected here in 1895. It was built on part of the site of the demolished Bell Hotel, and the passageway at the north end of the building, is still known to many locals as Bell Arcade.

1912. In that year the Constitutional Hall in Guildhall Street was converted into a temporary parcel depot, while the Cornhill Post Office dealt only with letters. Parcels posted in Guildhall Street were normally en route by rail within fifteen minutes of having been despatched. On country rounds, horses and carts had been supplied for the postmen. In fact it was claimed that everything had been done to minimise the strain on the postal-workers. The deliveries on Christmas Day were doubled and trebled as required, so that everyone received their mail by eleven a.m. There was a special word of praise for the mail-cart drivers, who had valiantly taken their great loads through to Thetford and Stowmarket Stations in the dead of night. The strings of pair horse vans galloping over Thetford Common in the dark had apparently been an impressive spectacle. What would those Edwardian postmen have said, I wonder, had they been vouchsafed a glance into the future, at the sleek red vans and mechanised sorting-offices of today.

THE DEADLY VISITANT

'Plus ca change, plus c'est la meme chose'. I walked into the waiting-room of the Health Centre, sat down, and found myself staring at a poster exhorting mothers to have their children vaccinated against whooping-cough. I had just walked up from the Record Office where I had been reading a pamphlet which contained the following sentence: 'A tender parent says, I shall never forgive myself if my child should die of the inoculated smallpox, that I did not stand the hazard of the natural'. The pamphlet was written over 250 years ago when Bury was in the grip of one of its all too frequent epidemics of smallpox. It was a fervent plea for inoculation by a local doctor.

By 1733 the town had been familiar with the ravages of the dreadful disease for at least a century. According to the historian, Tymms, there had been major epidemics in 1677, 1684 and 1718, but there is evidence that minor epidemics flared up with fearful regularity. In Risbygate, one of the main approach roads to the town centre, the base of the boundary-cross at the bottom of Chalk Lane acquired a special function. It was used as a bowl, into which people dipped their coins, into vinegar, it is said, to try to prevent the spread of contagion. The stone subsequently acquired the title of the Plague Stone, and, having survived into the 1980s, was well on its way to disintegration, when it was transported to a safe 'home' in front of the West Suffolk College.

Despite the known horrors of smallpox, which might terminate fatally or in terrible disfigurement, in 1733 people were still very loath to consider inoculation against smallpox.

The practice had been known in Asia and India for centuries, but knowledge of it had been brought into England only at the beginning of the 18th century. The doctors who tried to introduce it were ignored, but soon a champion of inoculation stepped forward who insisted on being heard. This was the colourful and talented aristocrat, Lady Mary Wortly Montague, whose own beauty had been marred by smallpox when she was a young bride. She witnessed the beneficial effects of inoculation when she was in Turkey, where her husband was Ambassador, and she was sufficiently convinced to have her own little boy 'grafted' in the Turkish fashion. In England, however, despite the fact that the Princess of Wales eventually had her children inoculated, Lady Mary met with an opposition that at times became hysterical in its violence. She was attacked verbally by the medical profession and the clergy, and in 1769 she was bodily assaulted by a mob of incensed women in a London street. Fifteen years after this incident the good folk of Bury seem still to have been opposed to the practice.

The author of the 1733 pamphlet advocating inoculation disposed brusquely of what were apparently the main objections to it. People obviously didn't believe that inoculated smallpox would give the same immunity as what they termed 'natural' smallpox. They were afraid of the possible after-effects of the 'prick', such as consumption, boils, blotches and weak eyes. They thought that inoculation might affect people with other diseases, and the clergy declared that the practice was sinful, as it was tantamount to voluntarily endangering one's life. On the positive side, the writer put forward several strong reasons for the immediate introduction of inoculation. The first of these was that the town's prosperity was suffering. He calculated that the current epidemic, if allowed to run its course, might last for two years, during which time the Assizes, the Sessions, and the Fair would not be held in the town, the trade which they normally brought being lost. That he was making a valid point can be seen from the following notice, inserted in the 'Ipswich Journal' during the epidemic of 1744: 'Whereas several of the Linen-Weavers who constantly kept the Weavers Hall in Bury St Edmunds with Hempen Cloths, are now hinder'd their usual attendance there by reason of the Small Pox being so much in town. We doe hereby . . . acquaint the dealers . . . that we . . . have agreed to give our constant attendance weekly every Wednesday at 10 o'clock . . . at the Red House, Horningsheath.'

The pamphleteer then went on to make an interesting observation which throws light both on the effects of the disease at this time and on a particular 18th century viewpoint which seems quite alien to our own. He stated that inoculated smallpox affected both adults and children similarly, whilst natural smallpox was known to be much more severe in adults. This he saw as an argument for inoculation, as 'everyone thinks the life of an adult, especially the head of a family, of more consequence than that of a child.' He then stressed the psychological damage to the populace at large. Fears and uneasiness for parents, relations, and friends. Distress at not being able to visit them when sick. The worry of having to neglect one's business. He finished by advising the inoculation of all children between two and seven years.

That this advice was not heeded we can guess by the subsequent grave epidemics in Bury in the 18th century. One of these was in 1757, and its effect on every household in St Mary's parish is recorded in a document still extant in Bury Record Office, a perusal of which shows a remarkably even distribution of the disease. In Southgate Street, for example, 53 out of 116 households were affected. In Schoolhall Street 27 out of 57. In Sparhawk Street 5 out of 9. In Guildhall Street 37 out of 78. It was a democratic distribution, too. In Schoolhall Street the Honourable Felton Hervey, with his household of eighteen, had one member afflicted and five at risk because they had never had the disease. His wealthy neighbour, Thomas Singleton, with a household of sixteen, had seven inmates infected and one already dead. At the other end of the street, though, a block of eleven small houses occupied by widows and folk in humble circumstances had no infected cases at all, probably because the inmates had all been immunised by previous attacks of the disease. The town workhouse counted 80 of its 175 inmates stricken, with 9 already dead, but the occupants of the almshouses had all had the disease before.

It was to be well into the following century before Jenner's discovery of a vaccine against smallpox, much safer and more effective than the previous inoculations, was finally accepted by medical opinion and by the public and the dreadful disease was controlled.

The Plague Stone used to stand in Risbygate at the corner of Chalk Lane. In order to save it from the ravages of another kind of plague, (1980s vandalism), it had to be transported. It can now be found sitting in splendid isolation on the greensward in front of West Suffolk College.

SAMUEL BURY AND THE
CHURCHGATE STREET CHAPEL

Walk up Churchgate Street from the Norman Tower and you will eventually arrive at what has been described as 'the Town Chapel par excellence'. It is known as the Unitarian Chapel, for such it was from the beginning of the nineteenth century. In fact, it was built for Bury's Presbyterian congregation in 1711.

In the mid-1970s, thanks to a grant from the Historic Buildings Council, its roof was restored, and there was talk at this time of the Trustees negotiating with the Department of the Environment with a view to opening the building to the public. There were no developments in that direction however. The chapel was leased for some years to the Pentecostal Church. At the time of writing the trustees have just applied to the Borough Council to change the building from a place of worship to a multi-purpose hall. If their application is granted and essential repairs are made, the Unitarians, who have been meeting for the past ten years in the Friends' Meeting House, will return here. The building will not only be used for worship, in this case, but to house public events, such as concerts and art exhibitions.

Even a perfunctory appraisal of the southern facade shows us what a fine building it is. The tripartite design is immensely satisfying. High, arched windows flank an elegant central section containing a pedimented door, oval window with petal-shaped panes, and circular sun-dial. The details, too, are charming. Carved key-blocks around the oval window. Scrolled keystones in the arches, and rainwater-heads with the date 1711 still clearly visible on them.

If you are fortunate enough to be admitted to the building, you will find plenty to interest you. The pulpit is opposite the entrance. Behind it are two oval windows like eyes. A gallery runs round three sides of the building. In the 1890s four hundred people could be accommodated in here, in the old-fashioned, high-backed box pews. The first major alterations took place between 1915 and 1923, when the downstairs pews were removed, the space beneath the galleries being later enclosed.

The story behind the building of the chapel is as interesting as its architecture, for it is the story of yet another of those forceful personalities who have left their mark on our town. In this case the gentleman's name was Samuel Bury. He hailed from Shropshire, the son of a Dissenting minister, and he arrived in Bury in the late 1680s to take up his first post as Presbyterian pastor. He was a young man in his twenties, and he obviously had great energy as well as being a gifted preacher.

The town's Presbyterians had had a varied career in the latter half of the seventeenth century. During the early part of the Civil War they were cock-a-hoop, in control of both St James's and St Mary's Church and of the Corporation too. Then came the Restoration. The Anglican Church and the Presbyterians, like other non-conformist sects, were forced to meet secretly in private houses. If discovered, they were liable to fines, or to imprisonment. It was only after the Toleration Act of 1689 that they were free to worship openly again. It was thus a newly-liberated congregation of which Sameul Bury was in charge.

In the late Mr Duncan's *History of Presbyterianism in Bury* he lists the members of the first Presbyterian Trust who bought a house in Churchgate Street to convert into a chapel. Samuel Bury was one of these twelve men. So also were John Meadows, (another Presbyterian pastor), and Thomas Bright, described as a 'gentleman'. The wills of the two latter

55

are extant in Bury Record Office, and it is interesting to see how much wealth there was in this section of the community.

Meadows, in 1696, had a vast amount of property to bequeath in thirteen different Suffolk parishes. He left charitable gifts to the poor of six townships, as well as to the poor 'living in the street where I shall dye'. To Samuel Bury he left four pounds.

Thomas Bright who lived in Northgate Street, owned three more properties in the same street, a house in Cook's Row (now Abbeygate Street) and properties in Brettenham and Ketton. He left five pounds to be divided amongst a hundred poor people in Bury, and he bequeathed to Samuel Bury 'a picture or a landskepp now hanging over my great Parlour chimney'.

As Samuel Bury's reputation grew, so did his flock. In 1697, when he was thirty-four, he married a widow, Mrs Elizabeth Lloyds, nineteen years his senior, who was a notable personality in her own right. A native of Clare she had lived in Norwich during her widowhood, and had already refused three other churchmen, because she could not be easy in their communion. Wealthy and intelligent, she had a remarkable knowledge of medicine, was a diarist, and was described as 'a great benefactrix'. Certainly the disparity in their ages does not seem to have detracted in any way from the happiness of the marriage. She too seems to have been instrumental in increasing the size of the congregation and enhancing her husband's reputation. It is said that Daniel Defoe was an admirer of Samuel's and heard him preach during his stay in Bury in 1704. By 1711 the Bury Presbyterians could no longer be accommodated in their Churchgate Street chapel. A new and larger building had to be erected, the one which we can see today.

By a stroke of good fortune the records dealing with the building of the new chapel have survived. Most of the other Presbyterian records were destroyed during the Second

World War. We can read how in March, 1711 the Subscribers were enrolled and the Trustees named. Six managers were chosen out of the latter to be responsible for the buying of materials, for disposing of or reusing the materials of the old chapel, and for procuring more ground if necessary. Amongst the directions to the Managers were the following, 'To buy their Materialls for the most part of such persons as are Subscribers to the said building, and of each of these in proportion to their subscriptions, provided (they) shall sell them as good wares and at as reasonable rates as others . . . That all and every workman employed on the said building shall be an inhabitant of the town of St Edmd.Bury: And that in the choice of such persons there shall be a particular regard had to such as are constant attenders at the Meeting . . . That from first to last they shall putt and keep as many hands to work as can be conveniently employed together.'

By May of 1711 the seating in the new chapel was being arranged. Every pew, whether in the body of the chapel or the gallery, had to be the same height, and no-one was to be allowed to raise a seat, or any part of a seat, above the others without the Trustees' permission. A Book of Rates was to be made containing the numbers and the prices of every pew with their proprietors' names. The income from the pews was to be used to defray the expense of the new building. Anything left over could buy other necessaries such as Bibles, catechisms, books for the poor, or in the education of poor children.

According to the accounts dated April the 3rd, 1712, Samuel Bury, who acted as Treasurer, paid in all £832-10s-08d for the building. It was finished in December, 1711 and opened on the thirteenth of that month, Samuel Bury preaching two lengthy sermons on that momentous day.

By 1717 it was reckoned that the Presbyterian congregation numbered seven hundred, and their pastor was in great demand as a preacher throughout Suffolk. He was not a fit man, however, suffering greatly from that painful affliction, 'the stone', and in 1719 he went on a health-seeking visit to Bath. Before he returned to Bury, he had been offered a new pastorship in Bristol over a congregation of sixteen hundred. He decided to go there 'to make a tryal of the waters' for six months.

To his heartbroken Bury flock he made a handsome parting gift of four silver chalices, four silver plates, and two large flagons as communion-plate. He also promised that, after his death, they would receive five boxed and lettered volumes of Mr Henry's *Annotations Upon The Scriptures*, to be kept in the vestry or some other convenient place 'for the common edification.'

Samuel lost his wife only a month after they had moved to Bristol. He survived her by ten years and they are both buried in St James's Churchyard there. One wonders whether he ever regretted leaving the town and the county on which he had made such an impression during the score of years he spent there.

The Unitarian Chapel. This redbrick building, acclaimed by Norman Scarfe as 'exuberant and fine', and by the late Alec Clifton-Taylor as 'a nonconformist chapel of quite unusual distinction' has been neglected for years. There are hopeful signs that this sad state of affairs will soon come to an end.

THE MARKET CROSS PLAYHOUSE

Bury's Market Cross is one of the town's prime tourist attractions. In recent years it has also become a prime target for what are euphemistically termed 'grafitti-artists'. This explains why, at the time of writing, the north face of this marvellous building is concealed behind a protective screen. I can see that this is baffling the early tourists, who are already disconcerted by finding that the Market Cross is no cross, but a substantial building, the lower part of which houses a building-society's premises, while the upper storey is now Bury St Edmunds Art Gallery. Even more puzzling for them is the fact that some locals still refer to the Market Cross as the 'Town Hall', since it served that function between 1840 and 1908, and the title stuck thereafter.

Before 1840 the Market Cross building had had a varied career over two-and-a-half centuries. It had been burned down, rebuilt, and had undergone several major reparations and restorations. The most important of these, was its virtual rebuilding in the 1770s to the design of Robert Adam. This gave it the appearance which, thanks to skilful restoration and valiant battles by Bury's preservationists, it retains today. This rebuilding took place during what surely must have been the liveliest and most colourful phase of the old Market Cross's existence, for it was then that it housed Bury's play-house on its upper floor.

We find a reference to 'the playhouse over the Market Cross' as early as 1734. The scholars of the Free Grammar School were then being given leave to act their plays there. By the 1770s the theatre was on the circuit of the Norwich

Company of Comedians, which also visited Yarmouth, Colchester, Ipswich, Cambridge, and Stourbridge. They normally arrived in Bury for the renowned October Fair, providing a varied repertoire for two or three weeks before they moved on. In Bury Record Office, however, there are original playbills for the years 1776 and 1778, when the Norwich Company was playing in Bury in the month of August.

Although there are no extant plans or drawings of the interior of the Market Cross playhouse, we can assume that it followed the contemporary pattern, with proscenium, pit, two tiers of boxes, and a gallery. The admission prices remained unchanged between 1776 and 1793. Entry to the pit cost 2/6d, to boxes 3/6d, to upper boxes 2/6d, and to the gallery 1/-. The gentry monopolised the boxes, but could on occasions take their place in the pit, as did Addison's Sir Roger de Coverley. The gallery, however, was decidedly the preserve of the man-in-the-street, who it seems was as vociferous as he was impecunious. Nor was it voices only with which the players had to contend. An ominous-sounding advertisement in the 'Bury and Norwich Post' in October, 1782, boasts of the excellent qualities of the walnuts, sold by one Henry Fulcher, 'the well-known High-Flyers', which could be purchased at the theatre every evening from the resident fruit seller.

On a playbill for October, 1793 the audience were assured that constant fires had been kept in the theatre. So despite the comparative smallness of the building and the many candles and lamps which were kept lit throughout performances, the atmosphere could obviously become uncomfortably chilly. This was no small discomfort, when performances normally began at six o'clock and lasted until eleven o'clock or midnight. Yet the theatre was such a popular place of resort that those with servants had to send them there at five o'clock so that they could go in when the doors opened and keep the family's places.

During the last three decades of the 18th century, the bill of fare offered by 'His Majesty's Servants From The Theatre Royal In Norwich' remained fairly consistent. For example on Saturday, August 3, 1776, they presented, 'At the New Theatre in Bury St Edmund for the Yearly benefit of Mr and Mrs Holland, a New Comedy as performed at the Theatre Royal in Drury Lane . . . THE RUNAWAY. Between the Play and Farce a sentimental, crying Comedy (never performed here) called PIETY IN PATTENS or THE VIRTUOUS HOUSEMAID, as now performing at the Theatre in the Haymarket.'

The Company had a family air about it at this time, and included several married couples like the Hollands, whose association with the Company lasted for twenty years. However they were no inferior provincial group. They were held in high esteem nationally and were jealous of their reputation.

The author of 'Piety In Pattens', Samuel Foote, actormanager of the Haymarket Theatre, was much favoured by the Norwich Company. Although he died in 1777, his comedy, 'The Lyar' was still being played to Bury audiences in 1793.

The story of Foote's own life is as colourful and, at times, as extravagant, as anything he conjured up out of his lively imagination. A university man, belonging to the Devonshire gentry, he lost his fortune by dissolute living and had to turn to the stage to earn a living. He opened the Little Theatre in the Haymarket and courted popularity initially by his scurrilous impersonations of society notables. Then in 1766, while out riding with some members of that high society, he was involved in a terrible accident, which resulted in his losing a leg. He had friends in high places, though, and by way of compensation he was granted a patent to perform at the Haymarket Theatre between May and September every year for the remainder of his life.

There is a revealing obituary to Foote in the 'Gentleman's Magazine'. It describes his plays as loose, negligent, and unfinished, the plots being irregular, and the catastrophes not always conclusive. It is admitted, though, that they contained 'more strokes of keen satire and touches of temporary humour than any other modern dramatist', and that the language, though sometimes incorrect, was very natural. In short they were 'very laughable pieces' . . . which was obviously what the Bury audiences wanted.

There was stronger stuff served up, too, of course. At least three Shakespeare plays were performed during the Company's stay. Though the fact that in 1793 the performance of *King Lear* was rounded off by a double hornpipe, leads one to suspect that these might not have been the versions which we know today.

And what of the players themselves? Not for them the hushed auditorium and the audience hanging on every syllable. Poor devils. Think of the futile exertion of playing Hamlet to a crowd of today's soccer-hooligans. It must have been much like that. Yet there were occasions, too, when a spark was kindled in that playhouse in Bury. As when the girl, Elizabeth Simpson, daughter of a local farmer, became stagestruck and ran off to become an actress one day in 1772. She was to make her way to London, marry the actor, Joseph Inchbald, and become not only a renowned actress, but an author and society-lady, whose virtuousness in her early widowhood only added to her charms.

An impression of the capabilities and styles of the players in general can best be obtained from the columns headed 'Theatrical Register' in the 'Bury and Norwich Post', for these contain reviews of the current performances. On October 8, 1783, the Company, newly arrived from Stourbridge, opened with the tragedy of *Isabella*, but unfortunately 'the fatigue of the journey had to some degree impaired the memory.'

On October 11, Mr Bowles had given a fair performance, but was exhorted by our critic to look at the person to whom he was speaking, and not fix his eyes on the audience as though to court applause.

Of the pantomime, *Harlequin's Trip to Bury* on October 13, the critic could say nothing . . . 'as it is a species of entertainment too despicable for criticism; and though custom has long sanctioned it in obedience to the depraved taste of the rabble, it is an insult to a rational British audience.'

The Market Cross playhouse ceased to exist in 1819, when William Wilkins opened his new Theatre in Westgate Street. It became first a 'Public Room', then Bury's Town Hall. After 1908 it had a chequered history, being rescued on several occasions from the proposed desecrations of the planners. Today, in the Art Gallery, one can listen to music, watch films and enjoy exhibitions of all kinds. Thus to some extent, the Market Cross carries on the old tradition of popular entertainment.

The Ancient Theatre and Market Cross c. 1740. The Duke of Grafton's Men, a company of strolling players, gave frequent performances here in the 1730s, when the Clothiers Hall, on the upper storey of the Cross, served as a theatre. In the late 1770s the building was reconstructed by the architect, Robert Adam, his design including a new theatre upstairs.

'A GREAT PLACE FOR A MURDER'

The Great Churchyard in Bury is one of those perpetual bones of contention, to which various interested bodies return every now and again for a brief gnaw. In the early summer when the grass and weeds spring up waist-high, there are groans from those, who can't bear the sight of Nature running amok. Once it was even suggested that the whole 'unsightly' area be converted into a tidy council car-park, with pretty yellow boxes to delight the eye, and the jangle of coins to gladden the ears of those who hold the town's purse-strings. Fortunately no-one took this proposal seriously. The Great Churchyard is one of the most interesting and delightful spots in the town.

In springtime the place abounds with nesting birds, and is alive with the songs of the blackbirds and thrushes, who perch on the old gravestones to feed their youngsters. While on misty winter afternoons it has a distinctly Dickensian atmosphere, so that even the boldest may feel a slight tremor of apprehension, as they gaze around at the indistinct shapes of the gravestones, huddled like so many sinister sentries. 'A great place for a murder!' a young nephew once commented with glowing eyes, as we made our way along the lime-avenue one late January afternoon. Nor was he the first to think so, as I soon told him.

It was on the night of the first of January, 1721 that the climax of a peculiarly sinister affair was played out in Bury's Great Churchyard. The chief villain and his victim were both gentlemen, moving in the upper echelons of Bury society. The driving force behind the whole sorry business was a combination of burning envy and greed.

The victim's name was Edward Crispe. He was born in 1672 and was described as a civil, inoffensive man with a stammer. His father had been denoted a 'grocer' in legal documents, but had obviously acquired sufficient wealth to entitle his son to be styled 'gentleman'. Edward owned land and property in Walsham-le-Willows, Chevington, Glemsford, Saxham, and Rougham, apart from his grand house on Angel Hill, and his copyhold meadows in Bury. He and his wife, Elizabeth, had four children, who were baptised in St James's Church, Bury. Elizabeth, born in 1699, and Edward, born in 1700, both died in infancy, and Clopton, who was born in 1702 and Isabella Maria, born in 1704, died in 1711 within three weeks of each other, probably from some infectious disease (although, in view of later events, it was rumoured that they had been poisoned.) Edward Crispe had at least two sisters, who survived infancy. Mary, who married George Roberts, Esq. And Kezia, born in 1680, who married Arundel Coke, Esq., Barrister-at-Law. It was this last-named gentleman, who was to be the perpetrator of the villainy that culminated in the churchyard on New Year's Night.

Arundel Coke lived on the corner of Sparrow-hawk Street near the Great Churchyard in a house, which was advertised, after his death, as 'a very convenient dwelling-house with out-houses and yards and a handsome garden, well planted, and very good stable . . . next adjoining to the Earl of Bristol's.' A daughter, Mary, was baptised in St James's Church in March, 1704. There is also a burial entry for 'Arundel Coke's child' in St James's register in August, 1711, (three months before the deaths of Crispe's two children.) According to popular account Coke was fond of high society and high living. Also, from the evidence of witnesses at his trial, he appears to have been exceptionally bitter towards those responsible for the South Sea Bubble débacle. So it seems possible that he may have lost money on this latter venture, and it was this, perhaps, that set him looking enviously at the money which his wife would inherit on the death of her brother, now childless.

However it was, Arundel Coke began to plot his brother-in-law's murder. He took for his accomplice John Woodburn, a labourer and a reputed thief, who had been in his employment for eleven years, and who seems to have been financially and morally in his patron's power. According to Woodburn's later confession, the previous summer, when Coke's family were in Ousden, Coke returned alone to Bury one marketday and sent for Woodburn to mend his copper. Afterwards he rode out to Saxham with him and told him, 'I have a great mind to set Mr Crispe aside . . . and when it is done, I will be a good friend to you.'

Some time after this, the first attempt on Crispe's life was plotted. Coke planned to waylay Crispe, as the latter rode out to his tenants in Great Saxham, by pretending that he was hunting and had found a hare. Coke would then hold Crispe's horse, while Woodburn stole up on him and killed him with his hook or bill. Meanwhile Coke's servant, Michael Mortlock, would be waiting at Rimer, near Thetford, with Coke's dogs, so that Coke could gallop there immediately after the murder and pretend that he had been coursing all day. Fortunately for Mr Crispe, however, he changed his day for riding out to Saxham, and the plot was frustrated.

On another occasion Coke had a key cut to fit the gates leading to the grounds of a Mr Fairweather of Rougham. It was intended that Woodburn should lock the gates, leaving the key in the lock, then lie in wait for Crispe to arrive and dismount to open the gate, whereupon Woodburn was to spring out and murder him. Once again, though, Crispe escaped by choosing to approach Fairweather's by another route.

Coke's final attempt to murder Crispe outside of the town was to be made when the latter was again visiting Mr Fairweather, (on this occasion 'to eat pork-bones'). Woodburn was to wait for his victim 'at the deep hole in Eldo Wood, on the left hand going in at the gate'. But as the would-be assassin rode up Rougham Hill at seven o'clock that morning, he saw, to his dismay, that the plough-teams of a Mr Evans were at work near the post of Bury Bounds, and that people were out raking brakes. When he returned to his master to report the sad tidings, Coke exclaimed, 'Damn this toad! We shall not happen of him now, but we will have him before we have done!'

Having perhaps become impatient with what he saw as Woodburn's bungling, Coke looked around for another agent to do his dirty work. On Woodburn's suggestion, he fixed on John Carter, a blacksmith, who lived behind the Market-place in Bury, and who was on the point of bankruptcy and likely to be jailed. Woodburn had told Carter that Coke could put him in the way of much employment, and on the 29th of December, Coke himself added several tempting bribes, persuading Carter to wash them down with a glass of brandy. When asked directly, though, whether he could cut off a man's head with an easy conscience, the poor blacksmith was confounded. Thinking to begin with that he was being offered a job as an executioner for the authorities, he soon saw his mistake, when he received the sharp side of Coke's tongue. Seeing he had mistaken his man, Coke dismissed Carter and sent again for Woodburn.

The last attempt on Crispe's life was painstakingly plotted by Coke. He invited Edward and Elizabeth Crispe, as well as his own sister and her family, to supper on New Year's Night. He stationed Woodburn, armed with his hook and half-a-pint of brandy, in a neighbour's porch, and kept him informed, during the evening, of the progress of events. While the ladies played cards, the men drank and became increasingly merry. At about ten-thirty, when the rest of the company was up-stairs, Coke persuaded Crispe to walk through the churchyard with him to Mistress Monks' coffee-house. As they started off, Coke gave the whistle that was his pre-arranged signal to Woodburn. Crispe, alarmed at the sound of footsteps approaching in the pitch-blackness, made his way over to the wall. Coke then walked back to grip Woodburn's sleeve and guide him over to his brother-in-law, warning him to take care to strike the right man down. To Crispe, who was unable to see what was happening, Coke called calmly, 'Brother, stand still!' Then he watched Woodburn bring his hook down twice on the helpless victim. Crispe shouted, 'God damn him!' before he was felled to the ground and slashed unmercifully. Coke meanwhile cold-bloodedly directed his accomplice to remove Crispe's watch but not his cash, as he rarely carried more than three shillings on his person. Coke returned home, a trifle out of breath, and told the company that Mr Crispe had taken a fancy to walk home by himself in the dark. He then poured himself a glass of wine. Was he silently toasting the success of his devilish scheme? If so, what must he have felt shortly afterwards, when the door burst open and the bloody apparition that was Crispe, came stumbling through. His nose was slit, one of his cheeks cut to pieces, his teeth and jawbone laid bare, and his throat cut in two places, but what must have been Coke's relief when it became obvious that Crispe had lost the power of speech?

This relief was to be short-lived. John Carter, the blacksmith, took his tale to the magistrates, as soon as he heard of the attack on Mr Crispe. And when Crispe himself was able to speak several days later, his suspicions of Coke confirmed Carter's story. Arundel Coke was arrested, and very soon confessed the crime and demanded that Woodburn be arrested too.

In the end both men were convicted under the Coventry Act of 1671 whereby an intention to maliciously maim or disfigure was punishable by death. They were the first offenders to be convicted under the Act, although Coke did his utmost to evade the distinction by pleading that his intention had been to murder, not to maim. He was unsuccessful in his plea, as he was with his attempt to secure a royal pardon. He and Woodburn were executed on the morning of the 31st of March, 1721.

Arundel Coke, at his own request, was hanged shortly after six a.m. in comparative privacy. Woodburn took his leave later to a 'full house' of sympathetic spectators who saw him as Coke's unfortunate dupe. As for poor Mr Crispe, he lived, apparently horribly disfigured, in his house on Angel Hill as a semi-recluse, dying a natural, and one hopes a peaceful death, at the age of seventy-four.

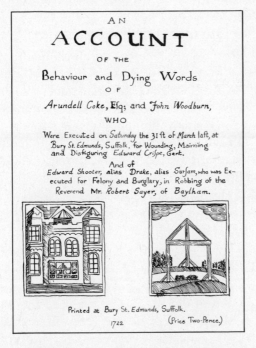

AN
ACCOUNT
OF THE
Behaviour and Dying Words
OF
Arundell Coke, Efq; and *John Woodburn*,
WHO
Were Executed on *Saturday* the 31 ft of *March* laft, at *Bury St. Edmunds*, Suffolk, for Wounding, Maiming and Disfiguring *Edward Crispe*, Gent.
And of
Edward Shooter, alias *Drake*, alias *Surfam*, who was Executed for Felony and Burglary, in Robbing of the Reverend Mr. *Robert Sayer*, of *Baylham*.

Printed at Bury St. Edmunds, Suffolk.
1722
(Price Two-Pence.)

Pamphlets like these were best-sellers in the 18th century. This one purported to reproduce two letters sent to Arundel Coke, while he was in gaol, the instructions to the gaoler re. the execution of Coke and his accomplices, and 'Mr Coke's Prayer on the Ladder'.

BESIDE THE NORMAN TOWER

I have occasion, several times a week, to pass through that gap between Bury's Norman Tower and St James's Church, a spot which, particularly on a murky winter afternoon, can fire the imagination. It was on this precise location that the 18th century establishment, known as 'The Widow's Coffee-House,' was situated, the supposed notoriety of whose proprietresses, has lived on in legend to this day.

According to the popular version of the story, the 'Widow', Mary Rookes, nee Haynes, was the daughter of a rich landowner. She was left with two young daughters to support, when she was in her late thirties and this she did by opening a coffee-house which soon became both the most ill-famed and the most prosperous establishment in town. When the widow died, her spinster daughters Mary and Letitia, continued in the business, Letitia eventually acquiring a more sinister reputation than her mother. To support the legend, there are two amusing pieces of visual evidence. The first is the drawing of the Coffee-House on Thomas Warren's map of Bury, 1748, in which the Widow's daughters are apparently beckoning suggestively from the window. The second is Bunbury's witch-like caricature of Letitia.

When one digs through legend to fact, though, a somewhat different picture of the Rookes family begins to emerge. To begin with, Mary Rookes' father, William Haynes, was no 'rich landowner', but a fairly well-off stone-cutter. As early as 1673 he obtained a lease from Bury Corporation of 'a small piece of ground next James's Church, excepting to fill five feet of ground in breadth for a passage to go to and from the steeple.' According to the church-register he married Winifred Dollar in St Mary's on December the 26th, 1695, and in 1696 their first child, Mary, was born. By the time William made his will in 1701 they also had a son. From this will we learn that he owned the 'Six Bells' inn at the foot of Churchgate Street just opposite the Norman Tower, 'with the brewhouse, stables, etc.', a house called 'The Old Tower' with stables adjoining in the Great Churchyard; and the house 'next adjoyneing to St James's Church' in which he was then living.

The last property William Haynes left to his daughter, Mary, who was then only five years old. Fortunately there is a surving Probate Inventory, which tells us something about the future Widow's Coffee-House and its contents, as it appeared in 1702. It was a spacious, well-furnished house with such luxuries as leather chairs, damask cushions, landscapes and pictures on the walls, and decorative china-ware on the chimney-pieces. It comprised a cellar, a beer-cellar, and a brewhouse. On the ground floor there was a kitchen, a closet, a parlour and a hall. There were four first-floor bedrooms, one of them large enough to contain two tables, two stands, seven chairs and a chest-of-drawers, apart from the bed. There were garrets which contained, in all, four bedsteads. It is interesting to compare this Inventory with the 'Particulars of Sale' for the same property in 1815. Here it is described as having a vestibule, two good parlours, a store-room, kitchen, washhouse and yard on the ground floor. On the first floor 'a drawing-room and three good bed chambers' with four attics above. In fact it appears to have altered surprisingly little in lay-out over more than a century.

Mary Haynes was formally admitted to her property in September, 1708, when she was twelve years old. In 1716 she was married in St Mary's Church to twenty-one year old Christopher Rookes, and in the same year her first child, Letitia, was born. We find Mary mentioned in 1718 in the will of her maternal grandmother, who left both her, and her baby daughter, Letitia, five pounds. Then in 1733 a horrific smallpox-epidemic hit Bury and in St James's Church burial-register there are the following poignant entries:

January 13th 1732/3 Dollar Rooks of Chistopher and Mary.
February 14th 1732/3 Carolina Rookes of Christopher and Mary.
April 14th, 1733. Christopher Rookes.

In the St Edmundsbury Post of October the 8th, 1733, the following notice appears:

'All Persons indebted to the Estate of Christopher Rookes, late of Bury St Edmunds, Innholder, deceased, are desired to pay their respective debts to Mary Rookes, Widow . . . The said Mary Rookes hath lodgings neatly furnished to Lett at her House next St James's Church in Bury.'

So having lost two of her children and her husband within three months, Mary Rookes began her career as proprietress of the Coffee-House. She was thirty-seven years old, and her two remaining daughters, Letitia and Mary, were aged seventeen and thirteen years respectively. Mary owned the establishment until 1760, five years before she died, and there appears to be no hard evidence to show that she ran it in a disorderly fashion. By 1769, Mary Rookes, the younger, had also died and Letitia became sole owner of the house which is described in the title-deeds as being 'lately rebuilt'. In 1776 Letitia decided to retire from business because of ill-health, inserting a notice to that effect in the St Edmundsbury Post, and in October, 1776, in the same newspaper, George Anderson, landlord of the Six Bells, announced his intention of opening a Coffee-Room, in view of Mistress Rooke's having retired from business. As in the Widow's case, so with Letitia. There seems to be no single piece of concrete evidence to justify the Coffee-Houses' notorious reputation.

It is not only the lack of any damning evidence that casts doubt on the authenticity of the Coffee-House legend. Letitia's long and detailed will, which she made in 1781 would appear to be that of a respectable pillar of Bury society. Her executors were Philip Deck, the well-known bookseller and printer, and John Symonds, Esquire, Recorder of the town, and Professor of Modern History at Cambridge. Indeed it was to John Symonds that Letitia left the Coffee-House, 'in trust, nevertheless, for Philip Deck'. Amongst her other beneficiaries were the Reverend Doctor Frederick Wollaston, who was to receive her silver coffee-pot and stand, and Michael Leheup, Esquire, who was bequeathed a round mahogany chair, while his wife received Letitia's best diamond ring set with seven diamonds. Letitia left several valuable pieces of jewellery. A purple stone ring with four diamonds. A 'small heart' gold ring. Four garnet rings set in gold and two gold watches, one of them her late sister's. According to a codicil to her will made on 27 September, 1781, however, Mary Welder, a relative, was suspected of having prematurely acquired 'certain watches and other plate' and was disinherited, all her bequests plus two hundred pounds being made over to Sarah Peep, an infant living with Letitia. This codicil has an interesting sequel. On September the 26th a notice had been written out for Letitia by Philip Deck, giving an impressive list of valuable watches, jewellery, and silver that had been stolen that morning. This appeared in the 'Ipswich Journal' on September 29 with a description of the woman – Mary Weldon alias Jealous – wanted for the robbery. She was 'about 40 years of age, black hair, black eyes, very much pitted with the small pox', and was wearing, 'a common brown stuff gown, an old bonnet, red cloak, and cloth petticoat'. Deck was offering five guineas reward for her apprehension.

In the 'Ipswich Journal' of October 6 it was reported that Welden had been apprehended and committed to Bury Gaol.

Six months later she was 'capitally convicted' for the robbery at Bury Assizes.

Letitia's instructions as to her interment were detailed and specific. She was to be buried in the churchyard of St James in the family vault, in a plain, baize-lined, wooden coffin enclosed in an outer leaden coffin. Obviously apprehensive of being buried alive, she stipulated a nine days' interval between her death and her burial and wanted no pall-bearers to attend her. She asked for a handsome tomb of black marble to be erected over the vault, with the names, ages and dates of deaths of all her family on it. And, with an eye to defending her remains against churchyard vandals, she asked that the tomb be arched over and surrounded by sharply-spiked iron rails.

It seems that, for some reason, Letitia's fine, marble monument was never erected. There was, however, a stone in the

The Widow's Coffee House c. 1780. The Rookes' coffee house was the substantial building to the left of the Norman Tower. The building to the right of the Tower was Philip Deck's Post Office. Deck was also a bookseller, printer, and stationer and close friend of Letitia Rookes.

74

churchyard in 1887, when the Reverend Francis Haselwood compiled his 'Monumental Inscriptions'. The words on that read:

'In a Vault near this Place
lieth the Remains of
Christopher Rookes
died 5th April 1733 Aged 38
Mary Rookes
died 16th November 1759 Aged 63
Also their two Daughters
Mary Rookes died 12th July 1768 Aged 48
Laettia (sic) Rookes died 23rd September 1782 Aged 66'

In 1982 this stone was restored by the Bury Society and the eroded inscription made legible. It can be seen on the exterior south wall of St James's Church, (the Cathedral), near the Norman Tower. Oddly enough, two-and-a-half years later, in October, 1984, contractors excavating for a new drain came upon a vault containing three or four coffins, close to the spot on the wall where the memorial tablet is fixed. Was it the Rookes family vault? Possibly. No-one can really be certain. Personally speaking though, I don't walk across there if I can help it. I make a little semi-circular detour. After all, you never know. And I wouldn't like to offend the ladies.

RED COATS AND DRUMS

The old Suffolk Regiment for many years had its home in the Regimental Depot at Gibraltar Barracks in the Newmarket Road, then in 1959 it amalgamated with the Royal Norfolk Regiment to become the 1st East Anglian Regiment, and this in turn became part of the Royal Anglian Regiment in 1964. Today the barracks have long been demolished, but the Keep still stands and behind it, every August, is commemorated the Minden Day Anniversary. The ceremony takes place on the Sunday nearest to the first of the month, the day on which the Battle of Minden was fought in 1759. The Keep houses the Suffolk Regimental Museum, and if you want to find out why Minden Day has always been a special one for the Suffolks, it is there you must go.

The story is a colourful one in every sense of the word. The Battle of Minden, one of the significant battles of the Seven Years' War, was fought between the British (with their Hanoverian allies) and the French. There were six British Infantry Regiments, the 12th Foot, (later to be named the Suffolk Regiment), being one of them. These regiments marched across the plain under continuous cross-fire and succeeded, against all odds, in routing the French cavalry. The French General is reputed to have declared, 'I have seen what I never saw before . . . a single line of infantry break through three lines of cavalry and tumble them to ruin.' According to some reports of the battle, it was before the advance that the regiments passed through some rose-gardens and picked roses to place in their hats. Another version describes the rose picking as an after victory celebration. However it was, the regiments who bear the Minden Battle Honour have ever since stuck roses in their caps on Minden Day. The Suffolks, (now the Royal Anglians) wear roses of red and yellow.

The Regimental Museum contains a figure in a replica uniform of the Grenadiers who fought at Minden, with the distinctive red and yellow mitre cap bearing the Regimental number XII on the back, and the White Horse of Hanover on the front. Amongst other interesting exhibits are thick albums of photographs, some dating from the nineteenth-century.

Medals won by countless valiant soldiers shine bright in their glass cases, the earliest dating from the Battle of the Boyne in 1690. There is an impressive array of uniforms, almost all of them original and in remarkably good condition, like the officer's greatcoat dating from 1850, with stout, unflawed skirts.

The whole upper room of the museum is vibrant with colour and the gleam of metal. Red coats and drums, shining weapons and silver trophies proclaim the glamour of serving with the Regiment. There are more poignant memorials, too, such as the board displaying photographs and mementoes of those members of the Regiment who were taken prisoner by the Japanese after the Fall of Singapore, many of whom ended their days in the horrific environs of a Japanese Prisoner-of-War Camp or while working on the notorious Burma Railway.

Throughout the centuries the Regiment has won honour and acclaim all over the globe. Its cap-badge of the Castle and Key (the arms of Gibraltar), is an acknowledgement of the part it played in defending the Rock against the French and the Spanish between 1779 and 1783. Its soldiers have fought in the West Indies and the East Indies, in India and New Zealand, in Afghanistan and South Africa. Needless to say, thousands of them fought and died for their country in the two great global conflicts of the twentieth century.

It is no wonder, then, that from 1878 Bury was proud to provide a 'home' for the Suffolks, and that, in the Abbey Gardens on Minden Day, 1944, the Honorary Freedom of the Borough was bestowed on the Suffolk Regiment, this being the first occasion that the honour had been awarded to a corporate body. It was a touching ceremony, taking place as it did in the dark days of the Second War, with a parade of the Suffolks wearing Minden Day roses in their caps and behind them the ranks of Home Guard, Red Cross nurses, W.V.S. and various youth organizations.

The figure of a Grenadier who fought at Minden in 1759, wearing his red and yellow mitre cap, stands with his khaki-clad modern counterpart in the Suffolk Regimental Museum in Newmarket Road. For anyone interested in military history the museum is a treasure-house.

The Suffolk Regiment's Chapel is to be found in St Mary's, Bury's most beautiful medieval church. It was created here in 1935 to mark the Regiment's 250th Anniversary. Here we can see the Battle Honours on the ceiling below the organ, and the Cenotaph to the Regiment's thousands of fallen. In St Mary's, too, we find the tablet commemorating the hundreds of Suffolks, who drowned when the troopship 'Birkenhead' sank off Cape Colony in 1852, and whose valour, in saving the lives of the women and children, (by refusing to overcrowd the lifeboats and remaining in their parade ranks on the sinking ship) has become legendary.

There are two other War Memorials in Bury, which remember mainly, (though not exclusively) the dead of the Suffolk Regiment. The earlier one, erected by public subscription in 1904, is for those who fell in the South African War. It stands in the heart of the town on Market Hill, and is a very fine, and sensitively-executed bronze figure of a wounded private of the Suffolk Regiment. It stands on a plinth of Portland Stone, on which is the inscription, 'Vulneratus Non Victus'. It bears the name of 193 dead, of whom 151 were Suffolks.

The second Memorial is to the dead of the two World Wars, and is in the form of a fifteen-foot-high Ionic Cross on Angel Hill. This was set up in 1921 and was intended to resemble, as nearly as possible, the cross that stood on Angel Hill before the Dissolution of the Abbey. On Minden Day, as on other summer Sundays, it is usually surrounded by cars and motorcycles, by family groups and crowds of teenagers, enjoying a day out. Which is, as it should be. Hopefully some spare a glance for the plea on the east side of the cross, which asks simply, 'Let those who come after see to it that they be not forgotten.'

TWO EARLY GUIDES

The tourist season begins early nowadays. A March wind was sweeping the market debris along Cornhill, when a man stopped to ask me where the Tourist Information Office was. 'Too early,' I told him, and directed him to the Central Library in St Andrew's Street in the hope that he would find some local guide-books there.[1]

Bury has been well provided with guide-books over the centuries. One that I am particularly fond of, William Green's, 'Description of the ancient and present state of the town and Abbey of Bury St Edmunds,' was going into its third edition in 1782. I find it particularly interesting because it shows the amount of new building and improvements that were carried out in Bury in the latter half of the 18th century.

Green begins by expressing the hope that the 'old, ill-constructed' pavement in the town will eventually be replaced. He then describes the improvements, which he himself has witnessed since mid-century. New houses had been built, of course, and 'additions and embellishments' made to others, but the most striking example of the way in which Bury had progressed, was to be seen in Cook Row, now Abbeygate Street. Up until 1750 'there was scarcely a shop . . . that was not partly or entirely open to all the inclemencies of the weather'. Even the largest grocer in the town, whose shop-front looked on to the market-place, had an open window, protected by a hop-sack against the snow.

[1] Since Easter Monday 1987 the Tourist Information Centre, now situated in a spacious building at 6 Angel Hill, is open throughout the year.

In 1782, however, there was only one open-fronted shop remaining. This was a cooper's. All the rest had smart sash-windows.

There were many exciting new buildings for the visitor to admire. The Free Grammar in Northgate Street, the King Edward VI School, had a 'genteel, new-built house' adjoining it, in which the upper master lived. The Shire Hall by the Great Churchyard was 'lately built'. The Theatre, now the Market Cross, had been built in 1780 from a design of Mr Adam. This must have been a truly impressive sight, with its white brick and freestone ornamentation still in pristine condition, especially since it stood in solitary grandeur, 'detached from all other buildings'. Green stressed the fact that 'as theatres are large and expensive buildings, there are few in Europe that exhibit a view of four regular fronts.' Opposite the Theatre, the New Shambles with its columns of freestone had been erected as recently as 1761, and the nearby gaol had been pulled down and rebuilt in 1774.

It wasn't only the recent improvements to which the tourist was directed in the Bury of 1782. There was justifiable pride, then as now, in those 'sites of antiquity', with which the town was blessed. The Abbey Vineyard, for example. Green describes this as 'a charming spot, well adapted to the recovery of convalescents and to the growth of vines . . . the vestiges of the parterres may still be easily traced; and the herb Alexanders, that was always cultivated in ancient gardens still maintains its place.' And, of course, there was the wonderful Abbey Gateway, fronting Angel Hill, 'a perfect study of the style of architecture of the reign of Richard II.'

Fifty years earlier, in 1732, an aristocratic visitor to the town, Edward Harley, second Earl of Oxford, had made a similar comment about the Gateway. 'The great Gate still remains, which shows the antiquity, as well as the beauty of that sort of architecture', he wrote in his 'Journey Through East Anglia'. He then goes on to describe with unconscious bathos, the Gate's present function . . . 'The rooms where the porter kept is a stable, and I saw a bear put his head out of one of the holes; it being near the Fair, those creatures are brought there for to be shown, and this Gateway is their general residence.'

This earlier 'mini-guide' to Bury is by no means as detailed as Green's. But the Earl had an eye, and an ear, for bits of local colour which today's reader finds both informative and entertaining. For instance, when describing Market Hill, (Angel Hill), he tells us that, 'Here in this town did live that infamous man, Mr Arundel Coke, who acted that bloody, wicked part upon his brother-in-law, Mr Crispe . . . Mr Crispe is now living in his house on Market Hill. He has no children, they were poisoned by Mr Coke. When I was at Bury in the year 1716 I then saw this Mr Coke; he had a very good appearance and was very well behaved and much respected by the gentlemen of the county . . . His widow lives in a small village not far from the town.'

East Gate and the Abbot's Bridge over the Lark. 'The river is navigable almost to the town,' wrote the Earl of Oxford in 1732. 'They were twenty years before they brought it as it is; they can bring up to eight or ten chaldrons of coals. The navigation is through Mildenhall and Barton Mills . . . It has been effected about ten years.'

Having dined at the Angel, the Earl described it as 'the worst inn I was ever at'. The landlord, Hannibal Hill, he dismissed as 'a great sot, being now quite stupid, whatever he might have been'. And the paintings, 'or rather daubings' by the landlord's nephew in the dining-room were not at all to the nobleman's taste! (But then neither, so we gather from his malicious innuendoes, were the Palladian building of William Kent, or the houses of Kent's patron, Lord Burlington.)

The Assembly Room the Earl found 'a very indifferent one, though much talked of'. Preparations were in full swing for the Fair which was to begin a week later, during which

The south end of Angel Hill c.1774. When William Green's guidebook was published, the Assembly Room was a three-storeyed building, with the top storey housing the all-important ballroom. St Mary's Church still had its turret on the tower, and the Norman Tower had a lantern.

time the Assembly Room would be much frequented 'by the County Ladies to show themselves and make their market'. His final assessment of the town's salubriousness was not a very favourable one, either. 'The air is very sharp in this town', he wrote. 'It lies high and the county about it is open, as it is all from Newmarket to this place. Fevers are very severe here; when once they begin they generally affect the inhabitants and make very great destruction.'

William Green must have been influenced by the Earl's opinion, for he also thought fit to cast doubts upon Bury's reputation for good, healthy air. 'Perhaps there is reason to believe,' he confessed, 'that Bury is not the most favourable spot to persons of a delicate consumptive habit.'

Plenty of visitors did find it congenial, though, in the eighteenth century as today. They were determined that Bury should be a tourist town, and so it has remained, thoroughly enjoying its role.

BURY HOSPITALITY

Our household is much involved in the twinning between Bury and the German town of Kevelaer. Kevelaer, with a population of approximately 23,000, lies near the Dutch frontier between the rivers Rhine and Maas, and is on the main railway-line from Amsterdam to Cologne. It has close associations with R.A.F. Laarbruch which is based close to the town. Indeed it was because of this latter connection, and via R.A.F. Honington, that the idea of twinning Bury and Kevelaer was conceived. When one reads the Twinning Committee's 'Brief Introduction to Kevelaer' it would appear to be an ideal choice, for the town's chief claim to distinction today is the possession of a religious shrine, originating from the 17th Century, to which over half-a-million pilgrims are attracted each year. Thus it seems a fitting partner for Bury, whose motto incorporates the proud boast, 'Shrine of a King', and which, during the Middle Ages, was one of the great pilgrimage centres in Europe.

In the six years since this particular Twinning Association was formed, there has been much reciprocal hospitality between the two towns. Groups with like interests – musicians, swimmers, chess-players, have arranged many exchange-visits. On one week-end every year 'Bury' goes to 'Kevelaer', or vice-versa. Close friendships have been formed. One, of our German friends has become so familiar with Bury and its history, that he can now act as unofficial 'guide' to parties of his fellow-townsmen.

The town, however, has not always turned such a benevolent countenance towards foreign guests. On January 7th,

1784, a nineteen year old French aristocrat, François de la Rochefoucauld, arrived in Bury with his younger brother and two travelling companions for what may be described as an educational sojourn. His record of that visit, which has been translated under the title 'A Frenchman In England. 1784.' makes for informative and entertaining reading.

'For the first few days,' he tells us, 'as we passed by in the streets, people jeered and pointed at us, crying, 'Frenchies, Frenchies'. This upset me a little . . .'

The French party, however, was soon taken under the wing of Mr John Symonds, Recorder of Bury, and Professor of Modern History and Languages in the University of Cambridge. He procured for them what we, today, would term, 'self-catering accommodation.' Although they received a certain number of invitations to dinner and supper, the French visitors soon came to the conclusion that in general Bury people did not care for society. Moreover, the society into which they were invited they found extremely impolite, particularly the younger members of it, who hummed under their breath, whistled, sat on tables and even had the effrontery to put their feet up on drawing-room chairs.

The paucity of invitations to the French visitors may be explained by the fact that Bury, like the rest of England, was struggling through an exceptionally hard winter.

'I have never felt such cold,' our young Frenchman tells us. 'It lasted for nearly four months, during which the ground was covered with snow about two feet deep and the frost made it as hard as the ground itself . . . Many of the evergreen trees were completely frozen, and the snow which settled on the branches of the fir-trees . . . sometimes caused the trees to split in half.'

That this was no diarist's exaggeration is borne out by contemporary reports in the 'Bury Post'. Already on December 31, a week before the French party's arrival, the snow had been sufficiently deep to freeze to death seven hogs that had run away from a farmer at Beyton. On Sunday, February 15 the postman going from Bury to Thetford was 'bewildered by the snow' and his horse sank into a bog, where they stuck until Monday morning. On that same night the post-boy and horse going to Brandon had to be dug out of the snow. Five days later, both postmen, travelling in opposite directions between Bury and London became lost in the snow, and, 'having had recourse to their horns', were finally heard and rescued by the family at Snailwell Hall, where one of the men had to have his boots cut from his legs, so severely was he frozen.

The severe weather was obviously presenting Bury with more problems than normal as regards the care of its poor. According to the 'Bury Post', on January 7, the evening of the French visitors' arrival, the young gentlemen of the Grammar School were performing at the Assembly Room, 'The Orphan of China', a tragedy, and 'The Minor', a three-act comedy for the benefit of the poor. Their profits from five nightly performances eventually amounted to more than forty pounds, which was distributed in bread and coals. On January 21 a subscription was opened 'for the relief of the poor of the town at this inclement season.'

Mr de la Rochefoucauld and his party, however, had little to do with the lower échelons of society. Conducted by Mr Symonds around the neighbouring country houses, they were introduced to the Countess of Bristol, to the Duke of Grafton, to Sir Thomas Gage, and to Mr Arthur Young, the celebrated agriculturalist, who was already well known to the young Frenchmen's father. They marvelled at the universal imbibing of tea. They complained over the length of the English dinner, which lasted for four, or even five hours, the first two spent in eating, so that, 'you are compelled to exercise your stomach to the full in order to please your host'. English cleanliness, as evinced in the ritual Saturday house-scrubbing, they soon discovered to be a superficiality, since both kitchens and kitchen-domestics were invariably filthy.

They participated in all the typically English sports such as hunting, shooting, gaming, horse racing and cock fighting, regarding the latter as 'a cruel sport, a relic of barbarism, which one cannot forgive in a nation like the English'. They danced at the Assembly Room, discovering that in England 'both sexes dance equally badly without the least grace or step or rhythm.' Their favourite recreation, however, was to play billiards in Bury's excellent billiardroom, which had been established by subscription of the leading people of the town. Thus the foreign visitors passed the long, arduous English winter.

Surprisingly Mr de la Rochefoucauld makes no mention of the event which was probably the highlight of that snowy winter in Bury. It occurred on Friday, March 26, when 'at one o'clock', according to the 'Bury Post', 'Mr Qauntrell's balloon, which had excited the curiosity of an immense number of people in the county, was launched from the Abbey

The Manor House, Honey Hill, (from Warren's plan of 1748). This, the town house of the Herveys, was built c. 1736. Since Mr de La Rochefoucauld and his friends were introduced to the Countess of Bristol by Mr Symonds, it is possible that they were entertained here. When the house was sold by the Bristol family, their crest was removed from its pediment.

Meadow of this town amidst the acclamations of thousands of spectators; and not withstanding the weather proving very unfavourable, (it snowing very fast all the time), it took a rapid flight to the south-west, quite over the town.'

It is difficult to believe that the visitors could have missed such a spectacle. Perhaps our young Frenchman, coming from the land of the great pioneering balloonists, regarded it as being irrelevant to his English education, and therefore outside his curriculum.

GAOLER EXTRAORDINARY

When John Orridge died in 1844, a respected citizen of our town, he received several eulogies in the local paper. He also merited an obituary notice in the 'Gentleman's Magazine'. This is not surprising when one learns that he was a figure of national importance in his own profession, a man who in 1818 had been asked to advise no less a personage than the Empress of Russia. It is surprising, however, when we hear the nature of his profession. For Mr Orridge was the town's gaoler.

His life is a striking example of how innate talent, energy, and enthusiasm can elevate the most unpromising job, for at the end of the eighteenth century when Orridge became gaoler at Bury, English prisons were generally sordid, even horrific, institutions and their keepers seem to have been of a similarly low calibre.

It was obvious from the start, though, that Orridge was from a different mould. He was twenty-four-years-old when he took up the post as town gaoler in 1798. The prison was then housed in Moyses Hall and in the Quarter Sessions records for that year we read of a series of improvements being made to the accommodation, all at the instigation of Mr Orridge. He asked for an extra room so that his untried prisoners could sleep separately from the convicts. He wanted a chapel where debtors could sit apart from felons. He was not satisfied with the 'irons'.

We are fortunate in having a detailed description of the old Moyse's Hall gaol as it appeared in 1804 to a correspondent of the 'Gentleman's Magazine'. The accommodation was on three levels including the basement. In the latter, described as a dungeon, were the convicts who were unable to pay for their beds. Here there were two 'barrack' bedsteads, one holding ten persons, the other six. The 'mattress' was a layer of straw, and other refinements included an iron railing with handcuffs, and heavy chains for the feet, (though these, according to Orridge, were rarely used).

Felons who could afford a shilling a week, were better provided for upstairs, where they slept in pairs in feather beds with sheets, blankets, and a coverlet. There were six beds in their stone-floored, unheated dormitory.

The debtors, usually treated as a superior class, had four bedrooms upstairs in the front of the gaoler's apartments and one ground-floor dormitory which opened off the court-yard at the back. They also had the use of a day-room, a work-room, and separate accommodation for their women-folk.

When Mr Orridge was giving evidence before a Select Committee in 1819, he recalled how unsatisfactory the old gaol had been. He had sometimes had as many as eighty male prisoners in it with no means of separating the different classes of criminal. There had been only the one, small exercise yard, and frequent disturbances. Even at this early stage in his career, Orridge was displaying those qualities which were to bring him fame. In 1804 it was reported that there was no employment for the prisoners, but that the 'intelligent and attentive keeper' was very assiduous to pro-cure it.

What had taken the 'intelligent' Mr Orridge into the busi-ness of gaol-keeping we do not know. We do know a little of his background, however, mainly from the registers of St James's Church. His grandfather, Daniel Orridge, had come from Great Barton in 1759 to marry a Bury bride. John Orridge's own parents, Daniel and Sarah, had at least nine children, of whom four died in infancy. His mother herself died in 1790 when John was seventeen, and seven years later his father remarried.

John's brothers, Robert and Charles, respectively eight and thirteen years his junior, were to be appointed trustees in the will he made in 1843.

We know that John himself was married to Frances Codd before 1800, for in April of that year his eldest daughter, Frances Elizabeth, was born. In 1801 Sarah Maria followed. It seems odd to think of that forbidding building housing two little baby girls.

The Orridges and their growing family were soon to move to a pleasanter location. For in December, 1805, a grand new gaol was opened. It was described as being 'at the end of the South Gate', and we can see the remains of its wall today in Sicklesmere Road. Here it was that John Orridge came into his own and was able to put into practice all the beliefs dear to his heart.

Security, health and morals. These were Orridge's three priorities in the running of his prison. As to the first, he could boast that after sixteen years in the new gaol, he had had only one prisoner escape. He attributed this to the position of his own octagonal residence, which sat at the centre of the radiating cell-blocks and buildings like a spider in its web. Nothing could happen in the prison grounds which would not be witnessed either by the gaoler, or by a member of his family.

The prisoners' health he maintained by proper medical attention, an adequate diet, and an insistence upon open windows in unheated cells, a measure which did not meet with the wholehearted approval of the inmates.

Finally he insisted on classing his charges not by their various crimes but by their previous character and their conduct and he always insisted on the necessity for full employment wherever possible. When they were employed, the prisoners could congregate with no fear of their being any disturbances. Only when they were idle, were they kept separated. The great treadmill, designed by Mr Cubitt of Ipswich, which was installed in the prison in 1820 was to provide a model for most of the other gaols in the country.

Orridge believed in rules which were not too severe, but which were simple and rigidly enforced. He soon abandoned the use of 'irons' as being cruel and senseless. He abolished the distinctive, parti-coloured prison garb because it destroyed the self-respect of those who wore it. He encouraged his prisoners to learn to read and write with 'prizes' of fresh vegetables from his own garden.

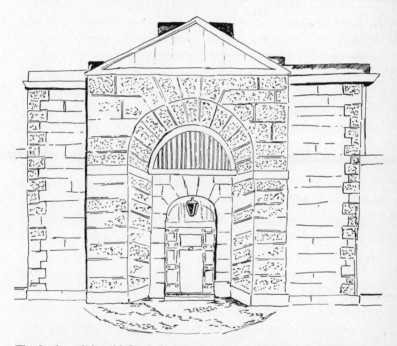

The Lodge of the old Gaol, Sicklesmere Road. Designed by Byfield, the Gaol was built in 1816, and criminals were hanged on the Lodge's flat roof. After the Gaol closed in 1880, most of the interior buildings were demolished. The Lodge and the perimeter wall catch the eye as one enters Bury from the south. Known today as 'The Fort', it is part of a small housing development.

Prison reformers such as Fowell Buxton were loud in their praises of Bury's Governor. Little wonder that Mr Orridge was the man chosen to design an 'ideal' prison for the Empress of Russia! By 1833, indeed, his prison could be described in a Bury guide-book as 'of a celebrity so extensive, little need be said upon the subject.'

John Orridge's three sons, all pupils of the famous Bury School, became in their turn, prison-governors. When their father died, they were at Cambridge, Oakham and Carlisle. Of his three married daughters, the eldest, Frances, married Patrick Macintyre, a well-known Bury figure who succeeded Orridge as Governor of the gaol in 1844.

When Orridge made his will in 1843 he had £6000 worth of property, including six cottages in Prospect Row to bequeath to his family. Perhaps this was why there was some local agitation after his death about the size of the Bury Governor's salary compared to his counterparts in other gaols and a request that the salary ought to be reviewed before Macintyre took up his post.

John Orridge died very suddenly on the morning of the 29th of June, 1844. It was a Saturday and he had gone early to market. When he did not arrive at the prison chapel for morning prayers, someone was sent to fetch him. He was found in his office, dead. He was seventy-one.

DEAR DOROTHY

While on holiday recently, I treated myself to a copy of Dorothy Wordsworth's *Journals*. The last time I had read and enjoyed her, I had been very young and living in Glasgow. Now in . . . shall we call it my 'maturity'? . . . I found myself even more appreciative of this remarkable woman's warmth, vivacity, and genuine love for her fellow creatures. As an added bonus to my enjoyment, I found that she had links with Bury St Edmunds. There was nothing else for it, I decided. As soon as I got home, I must follow up 'the Bury connection'.

Dorothy Wordsworth was sister of the more famous William. A doting maiden aunt. The mainstay of the Wordsworth household. A woman who worried over and suffered with not only the immediate family but those gifted spirits amongst their friends who flew too near the sun and scorched their wings. Coleridge was a lifelong care, always in ill-health, always, it seemed on the verge of a nervous breakdown. De Quincey, the opium-eater, was another. So was poor Charles Lamb trying to forget his tragedy-ridden existence in drink. Dorothy wrote to, and about them all, consoling, sympathising, loving.

However, she had other correspondents to whom she could unburden her own cares. One of the most faithful of these was her dear friend, Catherine Clarkson, wife of Thomas. She was a native of Bury, and she lived here with her husband, from 1806 until 1815, at Number Six St Mary's Square. It was here that Dorothy stayed on her visits to Bury. If we are to understand the deep and lasting friendship that existed between the Wordsworths and the Clarksons, it is necessary to know something of Thomas Clarkson's character and career.

Thomas Clarkson was born in 1760, son of the Reverend John Clarkson, headmaster of the Free Grammar School in Wisbech. He was educated at St Paul's School and St John's College, Cambridge, where he had a distinguished academic record. By 1785 he was well on his way to becoming just another brilliant scholar, a learned man of letters whose interests were divorced from those of the everyday world around him. Then Fate stepped in.

The prize Latin essay for that year, 1785, had to answer the question, 'Is it right to make men slaves against their will?' By the time Clarkson had finished his preparation he was so appalled by what he had learned of the slave-trade currently flourishing in the British West Indies, that he determined to devote his life to bringing about its suppression. He found support and sympathy amongst the Quakers, and it was through them that he had his prize-essay published in 1786. In 1787 he met William Wilberforce, and he became one of the committee formed for the Suppression of the Slave Trade.

It was to be a long and arduous battle. Clarkson wore himself out travelling round the ports gathering evidence, holding meetings and distributing tracts. To begin with, however, those with interests in the trade proved too strong. The only concession which was made, (this was won by Sir William Dolben in 1788), was that there should be a limit on the number of slaves carried in the ships. In 1789 Clarkson went to Paris at the height of the Revolution to try to persuade the French government to abolish the slave-trade. Undaunted by his continuing lack of success, he returned to England to renew his search for evidence on the trade's iniquities. By 1794 he was completely broken in health and impoverished by his efforts. Indeed Wilberforce had to start a subscription for him amongst his friends. He was forced to retire from his work, and a year later he married. His bride was Catherine Buck, the talented, vivacious daughter of

William Buck of Bury St Edmunds. In search of health and peace, the young couple took themselves off to the Lakes, where they were soon to be blessed by the birth of a baby boy. It was at this point that they made acquaintance with the Wordsworths.

In a letter to her friend, Mrs Marshall, in September 1800, Dorothy mentioned that a Mr and Mrs Clarkson came to dinner and stayed the night. Of them she said, 'Mr Clarkson is the man who took so much pains about the slave trade. He has a farm at Ullswater and has built a house. Mrs Clarkson is a pleasant woman.'

The friendship flourished. In December 1801 Dorothy reported several times that Mr Clarkson had arrived just before tea and spent the evening with them playing cards. Then, at the end of that month, Dorothy, and William (not yet married) paid a longer visit to the Clarksons. At this time, and for many years to come, Catherine Clarkson's health gave cause for concern. She was 'poorly' for the duration of the Wordsworths' visit. However, this does not seem to have prevented her relating a fund of comical and interesting anecdotes about her family and friends. Dorothy was particularly entertained by the tales of Catherine's Aunts Barnard and Harmer. They lived together in Norwich, not very amicably after Mrs Barnard's son had come into an inheritance which Mrs Harmer had believed was coming to her own son. ('Well I wish it may do him any good,' was apparently Mrs Harmer's frequent iteration.) Mr Clarkson had his own contribution to make in his memories of a Wisbech boyhood, including the cruel sport of bull-baiting.

From then on the coming and going between the two families was continuous. If they did not visit, Dorothy and Catherine wrote. By the time the Wordsworth's first child, John, was born Catherine had had to go back home to Bury for health reasons. Dorothy, writing to her in July, 1803, was very concerned about how she had stood the journey, and what the opinion of the physicians was. She was sorry, too, for poor Mr Clarkson, left in his solitude working on his 'Portraiture of Quakerism'. Dorothy had obviously made the acquaintance of Catherine's parents by this time, for she sent them her respects. She also sent her love to Catherine's sixteen-year-old brother, Robert, 'who is a huge favourite of mine, little though he be.'

Dorothy always held Catherine's father, William Buck in very high regard. He was a gentleman of strong religious principles and of some importance in Bury. At this time, 1803, he was in his mid-fifties and was being forced to change direction as far as occupation was concerned. The yarn-trade, in which he had been engaged, was now dead. He was soon to establish the Suffolk and General Insurance Office. In 1805 he was to join a certain Benjamin Greene in the re-opening of a disused brewery in Westgate Street.

Dorothy's admiration for William Buck, though, was for the practical Christian, the pillar of the Independent Chapel in Whiting Street, who in January, 1807, gave a dinner of boiled beef and plum-puddings to over a hundred charity children of Protestant Dissenters and who in 1813 was working for 'the early and universal instruction of the children of the poor.'

Her interest in Catherine's brothers was maternally inquisitive. In 1813 she was glad to hear that Robert was doing well at his Nowton Hall farm, but wondering why he did not choose a wife 'to grace his pretty dwelling'. By then she had decided that thirty-five-year old Samuel was her favourite of the four brothers and was wishing that he too had a good wife 'to make him as happy as he deserves to be'. (In fact none of Catherine's brothers ever married.)

When the Clarksons finally moved to Bury, the Wordsworths missed them sadly. The sight of 'the white spot at the foot of Ullswater' (the Clarkson's old farmhouse) was a constant grief. By now, however, Thomas Clarkson was back in harness and travelling the country agitating for Abolition. In March, 1807, victory was finally achieved. The Bill for Abolition received the Royal Assent, and Wilberforce made a remark which was sadly to be forgotten all too soon. 'Thomas,' he said, 'took the field before any of us.'

News and passengers travelled back and forward frequently between the Lakes and Bury. The Wordsworths were very fond of Tom, the Clarksons' son. Catherine, Wordsworth's fourth daughter, was Catherine Clarkson's godchild. There was news of children, news of literary labours, news of Dorothy's household trials and chores. Then in August, 1810, Dorothy paid her first visit to St Mary's Square.

'I like this house very much,' she wrote to William. 'It is just the same as being in a village'. She had been there for two days and had seen the Churchyard by moonlight. She had also walked, while Catherine rode, to 'that nice old-fashioned place with the garden, near a heath' (surely Hardwick!) There was still concern about her 'dear friend's health, though. Catherine had to remain in bed until noon, and Dorothy, who had heard that she had grown fatter, found her 'shrunken and thin'. In the kitchen by candlelight she had felt more optimistic, for Catherine had looked quite beautiful, with flushed cheeks and a vivacious expression. In next morning's daylight, however, she changed her opinion again.

After this visit Dorothy had many new Bury acquaintances to enquire after in her letters. There were the Mapletofts who lived next door at Number Seven, St Mary's Square, Miss Dolben, the daughter of the Sir William Dolben, who had won that first small victory for the Abolitionists back in 1788. There was Mrs Kitchener 'and her dear boys', Mrs Malkin, wife of the Grammar School's headmaster, and her son, Frederick. There was Georgina and Sara Gower.

The Dolbens, who lived next door to the Clarksons at Number Five, must have been interesting neighbours. Old Sir William, who died in 1814 at eighty-eight, was reportedly a great conversationalist and in his latter days a composer of Latin poetry. Poor Miss Dolben, though, was giving cause for alarm in 1811 because of 'a decided turn towards religious contemplation'. Catherine was apprehensive that she might overstrain her mind, since there was a tendency to melancholy in the family.

In May, 1811 Dorothy wrote a light-hearted letter to her friend explaining how she had cut up and re-made two pairs of Tom Clarkson's trousers for little Tom and John Wordsworth. A little over a year later came the first of two staggering blows which were to change her whole outlook on

The Clarksons' House, St Mary's Square. Thomas and Catherine Clarkson lived at Number Six, St Mary's Square from 1806 until 1815. Sir William Dolben, the Abolitionist, lived at Number Five with his daughter. A family called Mapletoft lived at Number Seven.

life. Dorothy had been left in charge of the Wordsworth children, while William and his wife were away from home. Three-year-old Catherine, who seems to have suffered from some form of epilepsy, started taking convulsions one night. By the morning, she was dead. Fiercely loving aunt as she was, Dorothy was devastated by this blow. As though Fate had not been cruel enough, history was to repeat itself the following December. For six-year-old Tom, Dorothy's blue-eyed darling was to die of the measles, again during his parents' absence from home.

In September 1813, Dorothy wrote to Catherine, 'I never talk of next year's plans but I think of Death'. Her confidence, her 'joie de vivre' had gone. Two years later the Clarksons left Bury for Playford Hall. Thereafter Dorothy's visits to our town were limited to the half-hour she was allowed between coaches on her journey to Playford. A happy episode had come to a close.

LUCY AND AUNT ANDERSON

It is more than likely that Catherine Clarkson was sitting at home in St Mary's Square writing letters on Bonfire Day, 1805. If so, she was engaged in precisely the same activity as a conscientious lady, whom we know only as 'Aunt Anderson'. Aunt Anderson was, at that time, looking after the welfare of a young girl called Lucy Watt and on November 5, she put pen to paper and wrote a letter to Lucy's mother in Jamaica, mainly about Lucy, but with little snippets about herself and her friends thrown in.

Lucy's father was a doctor in Montego Bay and she had been sent back to England with her servant, Black Peggy, perhaps for her health's sake, maybe simply because her parents wanted her to be educated in England. However it was, she was then a pupil at Mesdames Wood's and Green's Boarding School in Chequer Square, Bury. Through the public-spiritedness of her descendants, who have deposited her few letters, bills, and inventories, in the Suffolk Record Office, we can learn something of her life, and of the circle in which she moved.

The mail between England and Jamaica was in transit for a good three or four months at this time, as not only the hazards of the voyage itself had to be contended with, but hostile French warships as well. So when Lucy had expressed a wish to send a letter and two hand-painted boxes to her mother, her aunt had had to make arrangements for them to go by the Fleet. She informed Lucy's mother of this, she also told her what a favourite her daughter was with her two teachers. So much so that they had taken her with them to spend a week with a wealthy family at Soham.

Lucy's Christmas holidays were to be spent with different sets of relatives, in Quy in Cambridgeshire, and in London. Aunt Anderson, a single woman without any settled abode apparently, was writing her letter from the home of a Mrs Prince (a mutual friend), near Brighthelmstone. She referred sadly to her hostess's unhappy position, in being recently deserted by her husband. This had resulted in her daughter, a close friend of young Lucy's, being removed from the Bury boarding-school, which had caused Lucy much grief.

Aunt Anderson had personal worries in connection with Lucy, which she felt obliged to raise in her letter. She would soon have to pay the girl's fees for the next term and 'unless Dr Watt sends me a Remittance shortly, I am sorry to say, I know not how I shall be able to keep her there, as I have already considerably exceeded my annual Income, and am in Debt – which is very uncomfortable to me, or I would not have said a word on the subject, having our dear Girl's improvement much at heart.'

While her aunt was at Mrs Prince's, Lucy had no doubt been enjoying the various celebrations taking place in Bury to mark the victory at Trafalgar. As soon as the great news had arrived in the town, the Alderman had hastily summoned the members of the Corporation and they had walked in civic procession from the Guildhall to the Angel Inn. The Volunteer Corps were assembled on Angel Hill and they had fired three resounding vollies, which must surely have rattled the windows of Lucy's boarding-school in nearby Chequer Square. After this fine military demonstration, the residents of Bury joined soldiers and civic dignitaries in publicly toasting the gallant victors of Trafalgar. The festivities carried on into the evening, though all was not unmarred joy. Some 'wanton boys' threw a firework at the horses of the mailcoach as it stood outside the Greyhound Inn, causing the animals to bolt the whole length of the street and break the pole of the coach in the wall of the 'White Lion.'

The national joy at the victory of Trafalgar, was naturally mingled with grief over Lord Nelson's death and in a letter, written by Lucy to her mother in March, 1806, she told how she and Aunt Anderson went up to London to see the funeral of Nelson on January the 9th. They managed to secure an excellent viewpoint, and Lucy was suitably impressed by the mammoth procession, of which it was said, that the head had reached its destination at St Paul's, before the rear began to move from the Admiralty. However, in typical schoolgirl fashion, Lucy dismissed the funeral in a few words and proceeded to those affairs which really concerned her. First of

The Churchyard c. 1804. 'The memorials for the dead are very numerous' says White's *Directory* of 1844. So it was in Lucy's day also. The Borough Cemetery, after all, did not open until 1855. But the houses built into the West Front of the Abbey are not all that different from those we see today.

all, she had been ill, quite seriously so, with one of those dreaded 'fevers', which are forever recurring to threaten Jane Austen's characters. Lucy's illness had lasted a month and since she had caught it in London, she had had to remain there and be nursed, with great kindness by her London relatives. She was still with them as she wrote her letter, and had been busy in her convalescence making a 'habit shirt' (a kind of undergarment) for her mother. This and some pencil drawings were being forwarded with the Fleet.

Aunt Anderson had had a sickly winter, too, with her 'spasms', and poor Black Peggy, suffering the rigours of an English winter in Quy, was wishing very much to return to Jamaica.

Lucy asked after her two brothers, Alexander and Robert, remarking petulantly of the latter, that he had promised he would be a good correspondent, but had favoured her with only one letter since he had left England with his regiment.

By the 13th of November, 1806, arrangements were afoot to send Lucy and Black Peggy back to Jamaica, and a letter from a Captain Kilgour to Aunt Anderson gives us the details. Captain Kitchen, Master of the 'William Lushington', was willing to give Lucy and Peggy a passage, the cost of which was to be £73-10s. Mrs Kitchen was travelling to Portsmouth to join the ship and could bring Lucy with her. There was also a Mrs Hall, 'a genteel good woman', making the trip with her family, and she would be pleasant company for the girl.

On the 15th of November a letter from Mesdames Wood and Green to Aunt Anderson confirmed that Lucy was to leave Bury the next morning for Quy: 'Time presses and we really hold it as of such consequence that she should have some agreeable Females as companions on her voyage.' They had, they asserted, done all in their power to render Lucy as accomplished as possible and their wishes for her happiness would not cease with their 'adieux'. Lucy's trunk was to follow her the next week, being taken up to London by Catchpole's Waggon, which would leave Bury on Thursday and arrive in London on Saturday evening.

On December the 17th, Aunt Anderson wrote to Lucy's mother to tell her that Lucy was leaving with Mrs Hall for Portsmouth the next day. We can assume that Lucy's parents had been taken aback and alarmed at the news that their daughter was being despatched in the middle of an English winter on the perilous sea voyage, for Aunt Anderson admitted that 'had her mother's letter reached me sooner, I certainly would not have let her go till Spring – But it was too late. Heaven protect her and grant that you may be blessed in each other for many, many, happy years.'

Heaven apparently did protect our Bury schoolgirl. For she and her trunk-loads of clothes, (of which the list is still extant), the dimity petticoats, the white muslin frocks, the pelisses, and tippets, pinafores and straw hats; the parasols and the boxes of colours; her piano; and poor, homesick Black Peggy; all did arrive safely in Montego Bay, where life must surely have been very, very different from what it had been in the genteel serenity of Bury's Chequer Square.

IN A CLASS OF THEIR OWN

Edward Fitzgerald was not a native of Bury. He only came to school here, for seven years, between 1819 and 1826, but since these were formative years and his subsequent life was much influenced by them the town feels it has the right to claim him as a foster-son.

The Fitzgerald family lived in the Woodbridge area and Edward spent his childhood years at Bredfield Hall. He had five sisters, three brothers and a pair of ill-matched parents. His mother, Mary Frances Fitzgerald, was flamboyant, beautiful, wealthy and ruthless. Her husband, (a Dublin doctor who had changed his name from Purcell to Fitzgerald on his marriage), appears to have been a mild and gentle man. When he lost his money in a coal-mining scheme, his wife promptly left him.

Of the three Fitzgerald brothers, Edward, known as 'Fitz' to his friends, seems to have been the most gifted. 'The Rubaiyat of Omar Khayyam', that inspired, free translation of the 12th Century Persian poet and philosopher, was the only flowering of his genius to have anything like popular appeal. The rest of his work, mainly translations, is little known. To capture the savour of the personality of the man himself we must look elsewhere; to the many letters which he exchanged throughout his life with friends.

These letters reveal a most attractive character, interesting, humorous and charitable. They show us a lighthearted young man settling down gradually into a comfortable bachelorhood, which was to be broken briefly by a late and disastrous marriage. For most of his life Fitzgerald lived in the most modest accommodation, with little luxury, spending what money he had on pictures, and with a passion for toasted cheese, which was a joke amongst his friends.

Several of these friends, to whom he wrote for most of his life, had been acquired in Bury at the Grammar School in Northgate Street, to which Fitzgerald had come at the age of ten. They were an intimate little group who remained amazingly faithful to one another, so that as late as 1867, Edward could write to the son of his closest schoolfriend; 'Airy sent me a Capital Photograph of Thompson, second Master of Bury in our Day. I shall send one to old Spedding, I think, to try and make him remember me.'

Edward's schooldays would seem to have been exceptionally happy, and he had a talented circle of friends. The closest of these were William Bodham Donne, James Spedding, John Mitchell Kemble and William Airy, each of whom was to make his mark in the world of letters. It seems a remarkable collection for a school in a small country town.

W. B. Donne was two years older than Fitzgerald. A son of Charles Donne of Mattishall Hall in Norfolk, he was to become an eminent scholar, writer, and critic, as well as Licenser of Plays. He was one of Edward's most faithful correspondents, a most entertaining letter-writer, and an affectionate friend. His life ran on quite different lines from his bachelor friend's. Donne married early, had six children, lived impecuniously in the family home at Mattishall, and suffered a crushing blow, when his much-loved wife died at the age of thirty-five. After his bereavement he decided to move to Bury, so that his sons could follow in his footsteps and become pupils at the Grammar School. This was in spite of Fitzgerald's disapproval, since the latter thought Donne's boys, of whom he was extremely fond, were subjected there to an excessively harsh discipline.

James Spedding was the son of an army officer, who had moved to Bury from the North, so that his boys could attend the famous school. Like Fitzgerald, Spedding went up to Trinity College, Cambridge, from Bury school. He then spent several years in the Colonial Office, before devoting the rest of his life to the study of Bacon. Spedding's devotion to Bacon, about which his friends often teased him, had apparently been nurtured in Northgate Street, for in the published list of monologues delivered by pupils on Prize Day, 1824, James Spedding is entered as reciting a passage from this author.

John Mitchell Kemble must have been a valuable addition to any social circle. The elder son of the actor, Charles

The Grammar School c. 1850. A renowned and enlightened establishment even in Dickensian times. It needed no spikes on its gate, and no broken glass on its walls to deter escapees. A local guidebook of 1871 lists, among the Grammar School's eminent former pupils, seven bishops, a Lord Chancellor, a Keeper of the Great Seal, and five judges.

Kemble, he and his distinguished family, particularly his sister Fanny, were all dearly loved by Edward Fitzgerald. John, no mean actor himself, inclined, however, to archaeology and philology. He became a renowned Anglo-Saxon scholar, and succeeded his father as Examiner of Plays in 1840. A quicksilver character, he astounded his friends by marrying the daughter of a German professor while he was studying in Munich, then returning to London to settle down to domesticity.

William Airy, brother of the Astronomer Royal, became the churchman of the group. He was Rector of Bradfield St Clare in Suffolk from 1833 until 1836, after which he moved to Keysoe in Bedfordshire, where he was Vicar until 1874, and where his friends often visited him.

In Fitzgerald's day Bury Grammar School was under the headship of the renowned Dr Benjamin Heath Malkin. In a tribute to Dr Malkin, which he wrote in 1854, James Spedding described the headmaster and the type of school which he ran. For his time Malkin was certainly an original. His priorities were not the acquiring of solid information or 'habits of judicious study', but the development of an independent and open mind and an intellectual curiosity. A portly man with a rosy face, he was 'majestic in demeanour and voice', but with nothing formal or pedantic about him. Spedding paints a vivid picture of the Doctor standing at the library window, looking into the playground, enjoying the sight of happy boys, and never interrupting a fight or quarrel, unless it had been pre-arranged and was being fought in cold blood. Malkin would never allow fagging in his school, or anything that smacked of domination of the weak by the strong. He believed in having as few school rules as possible. The cultivation of self-discipline was more valuable than that of obedience to an external authority, he thought. So there were no spikes on the school-gates, or broken glass on the walls to deter those who might want to break bounds.

There were occasions, of course, when the Doctor's halo did lose some of its lustre. Spedding recalled times when Malkin set his Sixth Formers exceptionally abstruse Greek commentaries, and then refused to allow them to leave their desks, even for meals, until they had finished their task. Sometimes he set them absurdly long translations to be completed in an impossibly short time. His most serious failing, though, seems to have been his tendency to have favourites amongst his pupils to whom were awarded, often unjustly, the high places in class and the prizes. On the other hand, a boy to whom he took a dislike often remained in the Head's bad books throughout his school career.

On the whole, however, Dr Benjamin Malkin seems to have been an exceptional headmaster, and both W. B. Donne and Edward Fitzgerald referred to him in none but affectionate terms. The older boys particularly were treated paternally, being invited to elegant little dinners at the Headmaster's home, taken to the theatre, and given a much-famed annual supper-party.

What, one wonders, did Fitzgerald and the others see of life outside the walls of that school in Northgate Street? For Bury was a lively place in the 1820s. In the autumn of 1824, for instance, the residents were warned to beware of the 'Duffers'. These were con-men, dressed as sailors 'of vulgar and dirty appearance', who sold cheap English silk to the gullible at a high price, by pretending that it was expensive contraband.

A favourite nocturnal past-time at this period was that of cutting holes in shutters and stealing goods from shop windows. (Whole streets were subjected to this brand of attention). Garden-stripping was also rife, particularly of vegetable-plots. Gigs, which were left unattended, often had their leather aprons cut off. And there were the 'Corinthians' to contend with. These were upper-class louts, who rampaged through the town, smashing windows, forcing shutters, breaking lamps, and wrenching off gates.

111

In March, 1825, the Grammar School itself was burgled one Sunday night. According to the newspaper report 'nearly all the studies appropriated to the use of the pupils, were entered and stripped of clothes and other articles and a sum of money taken from some of the desks. The thieves entered the playground by means of a ladder which they left behind them.'

Of course there were pleasanter, if equally colourful sides to life in the town. Monsieur Alexandre, the Ventriloquist, might make one of his periodic visits to the theatre. Townsend, the noted pedestrian, could be walking forward, or backward, or both . . . as he did on a July Saturday in 1820 when between Bury and Horringer, he managed to walk forty miles forward and ten backward. Then, in January of 1823 there was little Master Hubbard to see. He was sitting in Number 50, Abbeygate Street with his 'talismanic scissors' cutting out his customers' likenesses.

The group of young men, who took their leave of Dr Malkin in 1826 were destined to walk in illustrious company. Fitzgerald numbered Tennyson and Thackeray amongst his closest companions. Spedding became a crony of Wordsworth. Kemble and Donne constantly mixed with the famous. Yet one feels that the affectionate bond that still linked 'Old Fitz' to 'Old Spedding', when they were both approaching their sixtieth year, was of a special kind. It had been manufactured in Northgate Street and made to last!

BURY'S FIRST MUSIC FESTIVAL

A music-lover remarked to me once how depressed he would have felt, had he lived in a provincial town before the days of recorded music and what a comparatively small section of the population, mainly the wealthy city dwellers, were able to listen to good music then. That was how Robert Nunn felt.

In the 1820s it was Robert Nunn who catered for the musical spirits of Bury St Edmunds. A young family man, he was organist at St Mary's Church where he was to fill that position for fifty years. His eldest son, also Robert Nunn, wrote his memoirs at the end of the century and painted a fascinating picture of life in his childhood home, which was in the Great Churchyard in the ruins of St Margaret's Church. The Nunn family were all musical, the elder Robert's three sons becoming organists in different parts of the country. They actually had a concert-room constructed in their house, which could hold three hundred people, as well as an orchestra and an organ.

In 1823 Mr Nunn's 'Concert' was being advertised, 'At the New Room, Theatre Square'. Tickets were seven shillings each which was the equivalent of a labourer's weekly wage. But by 1826 the editor of the 'Bury and Norwich Post' was still able to write that there had not been a serious musical performance in the town for over twenty years, so obviously Mr Nunn's New Room concerts had not been very impressive affairs. This seems surprising in view of the fact that Bury was so well patronised by the gentry, and that it prided itself on its gentility and respectability. In 1826, though, came Mr Nunn's opportunity to stage a grander event. This was owing to a combination of circumstances. A new organ had been bought by public subscription for St Mary's Church and the new County Hospital in the town was in need of funds. To celebrate the 'opening' of the former, and to help the latter, a 'music-meeting' was organised at the end of September during Fair time.

The two venues for the event were St Mary's Church, where sacred music was performed, and the Theatre Royal where evening concerts were given. The new organ, built by the renowned Mr Gray, had just been erected 'upon a Gallery of a very light and elegant form' according to the local paper. Whether the reason was the organ, the distinguished company or the programme, crowds gathered outside the church long before the doors opened on the Tuesday morning of the performance. By the time the first note rang out, not only were all the seats filled, but the two-hundred foot long aisle was also thronged. Amongst the audience of around eighteen hundred, were the Duke of Norfolk, the Earl Jermyn, and the High Sheriff of the county. The high point of the performance seems to have been Mr Nunn's playing of Handel's 'Fourth Concerto', a piece especially chosen to show off the qualities of the new organ.

Perhaps fired by the success of his 1826 venture, Mr Nunn embarked on an even more ambitious project in 1828. This was to be Bury's first Grand Musical Festival. Again the local paper bewailed Bury's 'undeveloped' musical tastes, pointing out that there was no Cathedral choir, no instrumental band, not even a glee-club in the town. Was this because it was a comparatively small town, the editor wondered. Or was it that there was no commercial or manufactory wealth to support such enterprises? Whatever the reason, it made those concerned about the hospital's financial position chary. The Festival's aim was to raise money for the hospital. Suppose the venture were a flop? The hospital might be left out of pocket. To avert this possible disaster guarantors were asked for. They came forward with the handsome sum of £3000.

The names on the programmes for the Festival will mean little to most of us today, though they were well-known then. The singers were Madame Caradori Allen, Mrs Marian Cramer, and Miss Paton, Mr Terrail, Mr Horncastle, Mr E. Taylor, and Mr Phillips. The band (never referred to as an 'orchestra') was conducted by Sir George Smart, but was apparently composed of local players. As in 1826, there were performances of sacred music at St Mary's in the mornings and evening concerts at the Theatre Royal.

The critic of the 'Bury and Norwich Post' was quite rapturous about the performance on the evening of Tuesday October 7. 'From the first swell of the oboes in the Adagio to the

St Mary's Church in 1779. Robert Nunn, born in 1793 was organist and choirmaster of St Mary's Church for many years. W. S. Spanton described him as 'a notable character, full of jokes and taradiddles, with a laughing eye, a rubicund face, and a figure short and stout.'

last bar of the finale of Haydn's "Surprise Symphony", all was perfect,' he declared. Madame Varadovi was encored. Miss Cramer (the daughter of the band's leader, and niece of the great pianoforte player) delighted the audience with a voice of remarkable sweetness. And the Overture to 'Der Freischutz' was as perfect as if the lamented composer had conducted it himself. Did our Burians appreciate all this wealth of talent? Alas, no. The whole amount of the receipts was a paltry £242, about half of what a full house would have yielded.

The selection of Sacred Music at St Mary's on Wednesday morning would, I am sure, attract crowds today. Airs from Handel. A selection from Haydn's 'Mass No. 2.' The Overture to Handel's 'Samson'. And excerpts from the sacred oratoria, 'Joseph' by Mehal. The newspaper critic was again full of praise. The band and chorus, rising above each other nearly to the beautiful carvings of the roof, presented an impressive spectacle, he said. The audience did not, however. The body of the church was two-thirds empty and receipts amounted to less than £290.

Poor Mr Nunn. He must have been sadly disappointed, for there was no disguising the fact that his Fesival was a financial failure. Some said it had been a mistake to use the church. Others that the seats had been too dear, with the cheapest at half-a-guinea. Perhaps though, it was just that Mr Nunn had not yet had time to educate his fellow townsmen sufficiently into the pleasures of music. This was a state of affairs that he and his family were to remedy in the years to come.

THEATRE ROYAL

As a child I acquired a considerable knowledge of theatres. Of the actual physical buildings, I mean, as viewed from a seat in the auditorium. For my father was amateur-drama critic on a large, provincial newspaper, and, my mother being occupied at home with a younger child, it fell to my lot to escort him to many 'first nights'. We watched performances in all kinds and conditions of theatres. In church-halls and schools, where the acoustics were dreadful. In vast halls where small audiences huddled together for warmth and reassurance. In functional drama college theatres. Even in gradiose city theatres, whose glossy and awesome appearance intimidated many an amateur Thespian. In the end I acquired a sixth sense about the places, knowing whether I was going to enjoy my environs almost as soon as I entered the foyer. The faculty, I believe, has never left me. This is probably why, the first time I stepped from Westgate Street into the foyer of Bury's Theatre Royal, I sensed that here was a special place, a theatre with which one could really fall in love. And so it proved. From that vital initial manoeuvre of purchasing tickets, (when the greatest pains were taken to ensure that I would find seats to exactly fit my requirements), to the actual moment of entry into the incomparable auditorium, the feeling of participating in a special and pleasurable experience continued.

Bury's theatre dates from 1818. It is comparatively small, seating three hundred-and-fifty-two and is an architectural gem, so skilfully restored, that experts come from all corners of the globe to visit it. Attending a performance in such a small theatre, with its proscenium, and its circles, composed

117

of separate, six-seater boxes, one enjoys a close and valuable contact with the actors, (and by implication with the playwright), that is not possible in a large, modern theatre. Yet, lest anyone be tempted to dismiss Bury's Theatre Royal as no more than a charming anachronism, let me quickly point out that, thanks to the combined efforts of the Friends of the Theatre and of Mrs J. Trussell, who works for the Friends of the Deaf in Bury, a new radio loop system was installed a few years ago. This allows patrons with hearing aids to hear more easily the voices on the stage and is an amenity offered by very few theatres in England.

The history of the Theatre Royal is as intriguing as the present building and contains all the elements of a fairy tale. Of several fairy tales, in fact. For there is something of 'The Sleeping Beauty' in the story of a theatre, that slumbered from 1925 until 1959, fulfilling the humble function of a barrel store, before it was wakened by some dedicated people in the town. Greene King and Sons have stepped in several times to assume the role of Fairy Godmother to a deserving Cinderella, as they did in 1975 when they granted a 999-year lease of the building to the National Trust, that stalwart Prince Charming, who battles so persistently for our heritage, for a 'peppercorn' rent.

But to begin at the beginning. How does Bury come to own such a treasure, one so curiously positioned in a rather out-of-the-way corner of the town? The answer is, quite simply, that it asked for it. At least, that was how it seemed to Mr William Wilkins, celebrated architect and theatrical proprietor, who had discovered by 1818, that the Bury 'seasons' of his Norwich Company of Comedians were far more successful than those in any other East Anglian town. Mr Wilkins, who leased the Market Cross Theatre from the Corporation, was thus encouraged to make the proposal to them that he would convert the present theatre into a public room at his own expense, on condition that it was never used for theatrical performances. And that he would build 'a theatre of ample dimensions and elegance, corresponding to the other buildings of the place'.

Who was more capable of designing this elegant building than Wilkins, himself, for he was then working on Downing College. He was to be, in future years, the architect of University College, London, and of the National Gallery. The only piece of land available to him was, indeed, rather out of the way. It was a sloping piece of grassland on the southern rim of the town, in Westgate Street. But Wilkins purchased it, designed his masterpiece, and built it for the sizeable sum of £5,000.

The Theatre opened on October 11th, 1819, the performance starting at seven o'clock. The price of a box was four shillings, while a seat in the pit was two-and-sixpence, and it was a shilling to get into the gallery. A measure of traffic-control was enforced, viz., 'Carriages to set down with the horses' heads towards St Mary's Square and to take up in the opposite direction'. The play being shown on that auspicious occasion was a comedy, 'John Bull', with a farce, 'A Roland

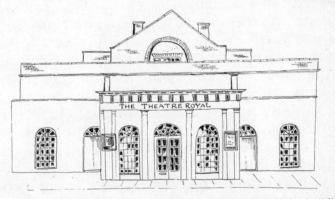

The Theatre Royal in Westgate Street. From 1915 until 1960 the building was used as a barrel store by Greene King Ltd. The Borough Council decided it would be too costly to restore it. A local action group showed them how wrong they were. The theatre opened again in 1965, and is now thriving.

for Oliver' to follow.

According to the newspaper reports, the audience was disappointingly small, despite the delights to be sampled within. 'The interior of the house,' one correspondent wrote, 'is very elegant, its form nearly circular, with two tiers of boxes, and a stage eighteen yards in width. The proscenium is in very good taste and all the scenery greatly advanced in execution. More light, or perhaps an altered position of the lamps is needed to do credit to the ornaments of the boxes, where sphinxes and genii, on the front of the upper circle, are the only part sufficiently illuminated; whilst a gold cornice finishing the species of viranda above, and the rich vermilion covering the interior of the boxes, are lost in sombre shade.'

Luckily business did pick up that October, and for most of the Fair week the theatre was fully booked. But as the nineteenth century progressed so apparently did the Bury theatre-audiences dwindle. In 1845 Wilkins' son finally leased the theatre out of the family to a gentleman called Abington, whom we remember today as being the man who gave our theatre its name. Having become 'The Theatre Royal', it survived, rather than thrived, until the end of the century. By that time its audiences were so unresponsive, that they gave the cold shoulder to that classic comedy, 'Charley's Aunt', which had its World Première here on February 29, 1892.

The Theatre Royal 'died' for the first time in 1903, but revived at the end of 1906 by the efforts of that dynamic duo, the Mayor, E. W. Lake and Alderman Owen Clarke. In 1925 it closed again, despite the efforts made by Greene-King, who had bought it five years previously. Its passing was lamented in the 'Bury Free Press' of April 25, 1925, where the advent and popularity of the cinema was blamed for the theatre's death. Doubtless no-one dreamed, then, that the Theatre Royal would be back in business again by the nineteen-sixties, and looking as healthy as its originator, William Wilkins, could ever have wished!

120

GEORGIAN BURY

I am a newspaper-addict. I read them for hours at a time, on microfilm, in the Record Office. Old newspapers, of course. Victorian ones preferably. Rarely do I come away feeling that I have wasted my time. On the contrary, it is more than likely that I will emerge on to Schoolhall Street in a glow of excitement, because I have struck it rich again. As I did, when I found the reminiscences of 'An Old Apprentice' in two editions of the 'Bury and Norwich Post' of February, 1886.

The writer, who preferred to remain anonymous, was recalling the town as it was in the 1820s, when he was serving his apprenticeship in a shop in Abbeygate Street. But it wasn't buildings, or civic amenities the old man remembered with such fondness. It was people. As I sat reading, the Bury of the 1820s seemed to come to life before my eyes. Here is what the 'old Apprentice' said about some of the characters who walked its streets.

'Poor Old George', and elderly shoemaker, actually lived in High Baxter Street, but was a familiar figure in Abbeygate Street. When old George talked of his 'Brother Bob' and the latter's legal problems over the sale of a cottage in Honington, our apprentice did not realise that the shoemaker was referring to a nationally renowned poet. 'Brother Bob' was none other than Robert Bloomfield, and George was his eldest brother, who had inadvertently helped to launch him on his literary career forty years before.

At that time fifteen-year-old Robert, too small and frail to continue working on his uncle's farm at Sapiston, had been taken up to London by his mother and entrusted to George,

121

who was ten years Robert's senior and a ladies' shoemaker. Living and working with other shoemakers in their noisy, crowded garrets in the City Road area of London, young Robert had made his niche. A friendship with a literary-minded Scot, a fellow-lodger, introduced him to the works of Milton, Burns and Thomson. When George eventually returned to Bury St Edmunds, Robert remained behind, soon to marry and to write his long poem, 'The Farmer's Boy', the masterpiece, which made his name if not his fortune.

In fact Robert did go on to earn a decent income from his writing. But he had the misfortune to be surrounded by needy and importunate relatives, George amongst them, who finally milked him dry. This delicate, gentle little man, he was only five foot tall, struggling against mental and physical illness and with a family of his own to support, appears to have been helped by his own kin to an early grave.

Incidentally 'Poor Old George' was something of a versifier himself, and earned the nickname of 'The Cold Water Poet' for some lines he composed about Thetford Spa when he was seventy years old.

Captain Goat, the proprietor of the Assembly Rooms, a 'stout personage', invariably on his faithful cob, was a well-known figure in Abbeygate Street. Once our young apprentice saved him from a nasty accident when he was riding across Angel Hill. The following day the Captain spied the lad in the Corn Market and rewarded him belatedly with twenty 'testers' (sixpences), a handsome gift in those days.

However it was an incident showing another side to the Captain's character which left the deepest impression on the young man's mind. He was once talking to him in the Supper Room, now Moyse's Hall Museum, when a stray dog came in and made a nuisance of itself. The Captain, as though in a joke, carried the animal over to a water-tank, sunk into the floor of the room, and threatened to drown it. To the perspicacious boy it seemed as though the laughing man was half

122

in earnest. This incident took on a new significance in the light of later tragic events, for Captain Goat was one day to commit suicide by drowning himself in that same tank.

The Captain was one of a trio of old-fashioned gentlemen, whose 'antique dress and courtly manner' had given them a reputation for eccentricity. Dr Mulless, a physician who lived in Hatter Street was another. A little old man who wore white gaiters, he was an active campaigner against cruelty to animals. At this period no-one took much notice when their fellows mistreated animals. Beasts of burden in particular were subjected to barbarous cruelty. This being the case no-one remonstrated when a young labourer in a cart proceeded up Abbeygate Street one day, belabouring a weak, emaciated horse with a cudgel. Unfortunately for him, however, he decided to stop outside our apprentice's shop, so that he could jump down from the cart and cudgel the poor beast more effectively. Dr Mulless, who was in the shop at the

The north-east side of Angel Hill c. 1824. The shop, and the absence of greenery in front of the perimeter wall of the Gardens, gives this corner of Georgian Bury an oddly modern look. Later generations were to fill the area in front of the wall with trees and bushes, which were removed in the late 1920s.

time, soon saw what was afoot and, picking up a thick stick, he went out to seize the labourer by the collar. Then he wrested the cudgel from his grasp and proceeded to thrash him until he roared for mercy.

Little Dr Mulless did not always emerge as top-dog, however. No doubt the whole of Bury heard the story of his 'Virginia Nightingale', an apparently exotic bird of many colours, which he acquired from a man who was dressed as a sailor. The man spun the good doctor a tale of woe, telling him how he had planned to sell the rare bird to a dealer in London for five pounds but was unable to go to him now as he had no money for his fare. The doctor finally agreed to buy the bird for a sovereign, only to discover very shortly that his Virginia Nightingale was no more than a poor, little painted sparrow!

The third eccentric was Admiral Wollaston, a tall man with a peculiar, one-sided walk, whose green coat was one of the features of the town . . . Unknown to this gentleman his coat had almost been the cause of his being accidentally shot one day. It had blended in so perfectly with a certain hedgerow in Horringer, that he had almost been winged by our young apprentice who was shooting birds with a new air-pistol. Only the fact that he coughed at the critical moment had saved him.

There was nothing dull about Bury in the 1820s. There was always something afoot. There might be a visit from the trickster pamphlet-sellers, who 'cried marvellous news' and always caught a netful of gullible victims, as they did on the day when they sold a totally fabricated report of a coven of witches being discovered at Colchester.

Or it might be the shoemaker's carnival-day, October 25, with the town consequently rowdier than normal. At the end of August the printers held their 'Way-goose' and would come staggering home down Abbeygate Street after their celebrations.

In Fair-time the Abbeygate Street folk had a fine view of all the goings-on on Angel Hill, especially on the 'Grand Saturday', when the gentry promenaded the 'squares', buying goods and visiting the shows. Duchesses, countesses, dukes and lords could be seen and identified, as they passed by.

The highlight of the year, though, for our apprentice was Christmas, and he had particularly vivid memories of one Christmas which had been exceptionally happy for him. According to his reckoning, he thought it must have been the Christmas of 1825.

As December 25 approached, the scene was a very different one to that which we see at the same season nowadays.

For commercialism was as yet in its infancy. The three grocers in Abbeygate Street, Mr Biggs, Messrs Ridley and Mr Adams, stuck sprigs of holly in their cheeses and butter-tubs, hung a gammon of bacon at their respective doors, and garnished the additional plums and currants in their windows

The south end of Angel Hill c. 1824. The Assembly Rooms, whose proprietor, Captain Goat, was a friend of our Apprentice, had been redesigned in 1789, and the top storey removed. The handsome new ballroom was, (and still is) much admired. The Angel Inn was another building of Georgian construction. Mr Boldero, the landlord, was a friend of the Apprentice's employers.

125

with nuts, oranges, and candied peel. Mrs Walton, the fishmonger, whose premises were at the back of the Half Moon Inn in the Buttermarket, had an unusually fine show of poultry and game. All along the east side of the Buttermarket, on the Wednesdays approaching Christmas, the farmers' wives took their stance with their baskets of fowls and their dairy-produce. These ladies were an impressive sight in their long cloaks and individual headgear, the latter designed with an eye to comfort rather than beauty.

The reason, of course, that Christmas was not commercially exploited in the 1820s was that the greater part of the populace found it hard enough to provide themselves with the necessities of life, far less the luxuries. Items such as tea and sugar, which we regard as amongst the basics of our grocery-order, had to be hoarded and sparingly used. When we learn that tea sold for around six shillings a pound, and consider that a man's weekly wage could be as low as eight shillings a week, we can understand why. Even pork, which was regarded as the working-man's meat, was often priced out of his reach.

As for home comforts, the mahogany furniture and elegant candle-lit drawing-rooms which we read of in Jane Austen's novels were only for the few. The majority lived with coarse wooden furniture and unlovely crockery, their poor room lit by a feeble rushlight, a kind of home-made taper. Their clothes were as drab as their surroundings, whilst such 'modern' refinements as umbrellas and Wellington boots were far beyond their means.

Despite their hard existence, people did manage to enjoy themselves, however, and the young apprentice was no exception. The particular Christmas which he remembered so vividly brought him much delight. To begin with, a friend in Norwich sent him a fine turkey, which he was able to compare, to his satisfaction, with those in Mrs Walton's display. He took it along in great triumph to his friend Mrs Elven in

Whiting Street, where he had been invited for his Christmas dinner.

The Elvens were a well-known Bury family. Mr Elven was a leather-cutter and at this date his son, Cornelius, who assisted him in the business, was a preacher at a small chapel in Lower Baxter Street. Six foot tall and weighing twenty stone, this young man was to become the dynamic and well-loved minister of Garland Street Baptist Chapel.

The highlight of the apprentice's Christmas was the party to which he was invited on December 24. It must have been a popular day for parties as his employers too had been invited to one that afternoon. They were going to the house of Mr John Boldero on Angel Hill, a few doors along from the

The Abbey Gate from the Botanic Garden c. 1821. Even in a state of semi-ruin, the Abbey Gate was still a thing of beauty. Much admired was the east window which had once lighted a room on the upper storey. It was another thirty years before the 1st Marquis of Bristol would pay for a slate roof to protect the Gateway.

127

Angel Inn. It was whilst landlord of this establishment that Mr Boldero apparently amassed a fortune. Part of his fame, however, lay in the fact that he was one of the stoutest men in Suffolk, and it was for his remarkable funeral, not for the fact that he had been a prominent Tory and once Mayor of Bury, that he was long remembered. When he was buried in 1838 it was said that the weight of his body and its 'encasements of wood and lead' amounted to one hundred-and-thirty-six stone!

The identity of our apprentice's hosts is not revealed, but he tells us that they lived in Risbygate Street, and from his description of their home they were obviously people of means. The prettily-decorated rooms, heated by roaring fires, were lit by an abundance of wax candles. When the young man arrived games were in progress both upstairs and downstairs, with the older guests looking on from their fireside chairs. A high-spirited bunch seated around a large table were playing Pope Joan, a game of chance played with a special board and counters. More sober groups were playing cribbage or whist, and there were sounds of great hilarity upstairs where 'Forfeits' and 'Blind Man's Buff' were in full swing.

Amongst the guests was Mrs Cabburn, wife of an Abbeygate Street hairdresser, reputed to be the loveliest-looking woman in Bury. There was young Fred Brown, whose father was a bootmaker in Abbeygate Street. There was Miss Fanny Stocking, the daughter of the curate of St James's, and there were the son and daughter of Mrs Blake, a widow who kept a school for young ladies at the north-west corner of Angel Hill. These were all acquaintances or friends of our apprentice, whom he probably saw daily. It is not surprising then that he was drawn to two strangers who had more to offer than the usual snippets of local gossip.

The two were an elderly couple from London whose names are unfortunately not mentioned for they certainly sounded intriguing characters. Our young friend had never seen a funnier old gentleman. His dress was of a very antiquated appearance with knee-breeches and a blue coat adorned with huge brass buttons and a snowy white frill at the breast. His hair he wore powdered, with a queue. Such eccentricities were surely permissible, however, in a man who had once dined with the great Dr Johnson at his home in Bolt Court, had met Commodore Nelson, had ridden in a carriage with William Pitt and had an acquaintance with Lord Byron and Thomas Moore!

At suppertime there was a fresh influx of guests, including Mr Cabburn, the hairdresser. He appears to have taken on

The Old Theatre on the Cornhill. In 1818 the Old Theatre which stood on the site of the former Market Cross, (hence the name of the building today), had been converted by the Corporation into a Concert Room and News Room. The Apprentice must have passed it en route to his party in Risbygate Street.

the role of the party's comedian, ousting a sandy-haired, young bank-clerk from the part. He bowled his audience over with comic performances, based on those of Charles Mathews, the Elder, then one of London's star attractions. Amongst the parts he acted were those of a dirty, little boy reluctant to be washed; a nurse imbibing from the brandy-bottle behind her patient's back; and a village-cobbler trying to fit a pair of boots on to a young lady who was afflicted with a bunion. It was all good wholesome fun, and the company loved it.

After supper, when the children had been packed off to bed, the mood changed. The guests gathered round the blazing fire, and there were songs and stories. The old lady from London sang 'Auld Robin Gray' and brought tears to quite a few eyes. The old tales of Bury ghosts and Bury murders were aired and found to be just as spine-tickling as ever. Mr John Dalton told stories about the 'resurrectionists' and the ingenious methods they used to steal their bodies for the surgeons. There was a discussion about the superstitious folk of Wickham Skeith, who, only a few months before, had 'swam' a pedlar for a wizard, because they thought he had bewitched two local people.

So the happy company talked and sang until the bells finally ushered in Christmas Day. Thanks to an old gentleman taking a notion to write down his memories, we have had a telling glimpse into the social life of the middle-class in Georgian Bury St Edmunds.

THE OLD SUFFOLK GENERAL

I regularly accompany an out-patient to the West Suffolk Hospital and never fail to wonder at the warmth and friendliness of the place. Certainly the building itself is modern and bright with cheerful waiting areas and comfortable seats. But there is more to it than that. I think it has to do with a rather special ingredient, which a nursing-friend of mine refers to as T.L.C., or Tender Loving Care. This is found in the West Suffolk in abundance.

When the forerunner of the West Suffolk Hospital the Suffolk General Hospital, opened in January, 1826 the atmosphere was somewhat different. At least so the 'Rules and Orders' for its management indicate. The hospital was supported by subscriptions and one could become a Governor either by donating a sum in excess of twenty guineas, or by subscribing two guineas annually to the hospital. Subscribers could nominate people for admission in proportion to the amount they subscribed. Thus, for half-a-guinea annually, one could recommend only two out-patients. Those who subscribed ten guineas were allowed to nominate five in-patients and ten out-patients. Only accident cases and sudden emergencies were admitted without a recommendation, and these had to be discharged on the Thursday following their admission, unless the Weekly Committee ordered otherwise.

Every Thursday, between noon and two p.m., the Weekly Committee examined the applicants, and many unfortunates were turned away, because they did not fulfil the required conditions. No-one was taken in, for example, who could pay to be cured elsewhere. It is recorded in the Minute Book that

Deborah Robinson for example, was rejected in August 1827 because her husband was a master bricklayer. On the other hand, people receiving parish relief did not qualify for entry as they were supposed to be entitled to the services of their parish surgeon. Applicants for in-treatment had to have decent clothing and a change of linen, so it is obvious why poor Elizabeth Young was turned away in January, 1830. She was, 'in so dirty a state as to be unfit for admission'. Soldiers were not taken in, unless an officer or some other responsible person undertook to pay for their keep during their stay in hospital.

There were a whole host of diseases, which, paradoxically, were a bar to admission. In the spring of 1828, Emily Cross was rejected because she had consumption. Petchy Pask was rejected because he had a reducible hernia and several cases of venereal disease were turned away. No-one with inveterate ulcers on the leg, inoperable cancer, or in the last stages of dropsy, was admitted. There was no place for incurable cases, infectious diseases, women advanced in pregnancy or children under seven years of age.

Of the patients who were admitted there were some who obviously did not relish the treatment and discipline, to which they were subjected. These were given short shrift. In October, 1826, for instance, certain patients in the mens ward had the temerity to complain about the food, and two of these were instantly sent packing! In April, 1829, a William Hunt was refused admittance because he had misconducted himself when in the hospital before and in May, a John Lennard was turned away for the same reason.

Those who were able were expected to help with the nursing, washing, ironing, and cleaning of wards. There was certainly no danger of the patients being spoiled by over-indulgence. There were strict rules against swearing, gambling, smoking and drinking. Visitors were not allowed to bring in provisions and any patient found secreting food, which they hadn't managed to eat at their mealtime, was immediately discharged. The inmates who did survive their stay (and fortunately there were many), were ordered, finally, to give thanks for their deliverance at a place of public worship after they were discharged!

If the rules concerning the patients were strict, those affecting the staff were equally so. The matron had to be a single woman, over thirty-five years of age and of remarkable talents, apparently. For not only had she to supervise the state and fate of all provisions and furnishings in the hospital, but she had to keep a constant check on the movements of the patients, taking roll-calls morning and evening and seeing that they did not exceed their statutory hour in the hospital

The Suffolk General Hospital c. 1850. The building had been a military depot, and a store for arms and gunpowder, before it was purchased for a hospital in 1825. It was described in contemporary guidebooks as being 'upon an elevated site out of the Westgate Street'. It was enlarged in 1847, and much altered in 1862. Today it is an attractive-looking residential home.

grounds. She was personally responsible for their diets and had to inspect the wards at last twice daily to see that everything was clean. She had to supervise the nurses and the servants, and keep the keys of the outer gates. This entailed locking up at nine p.m. in the winter and at ten in the summer. The career of the first matron, Mrs Goodchild, lasted less than a year, owing to what appears to have been over-assiduity in attending to her duties. She accused the house-apothecary of improper conduct towards one of the nurses, a charge which was strenuously refuted and subsequently adjudged by the Committee to be false.

The house apothecary, who was the secretary, too, in these early years, undoubtedly had the most demanding post in the establishment. He had to be over twenty-one and to have served either five years with a surgeon or apothecary, or three years in a public hospital. His duties were too manifold to tabulate. Amongst them was the physical organisation of the wards, including the recording of the number of beds available. The responsibility for the patients' records, the dispensing of medicines and the visiting of patients to note the effects of the former. The bleeding of patients. Attendance at committee-meetings. The keeping of the cash-book and of the register of subscribers. It is no wonder that the first two house apothecaries both fell ill through overwork and were forced to resign.

Rules for the nursing-staff were few and simple. They had to have their wards cleaned by seven a.m. in summer, and by eight a.m. in winter, and to serve breakfast an hour later. They had to withdraw to the hall, when the House Visitors arrived on their tours of inspection, and to be available to answer questions concerning patients' grumbles. Most important of all, perhaps, they were exhorted to behave with tenderness to the patients, and civility and respect to strangers.

It became apparent, at the end of the hospital's first year, that it could not survive solely on its subscriptions and in October, 1827, came the first of that long line of what we now term 'fund-raising events'. This was a 'Ladies Sale of Fancy Work' at the Guildhall and there was an enthusiastic report of it in the 'Bury and Norwich Post'. When the doors opened at noon on the sale's first day, the potential customers were enthralled to find themselves in an arcade of evergreens and flowers, with personages like the Marchioness of Bristol, with her three daughters and her sister, the Countess of Euston and Lady Isabella Fitz Roy serving behind the stalls. Apart from the painting and drawings to be bought in the Council Chamber, a model of the hospital was sold for five pounds, and a pair of ottomans for fifteen guineas. Such novelties as ink-stands made from Milton's tree in Cambridge, and dolls in national costume, donated by the Ladies Cornwallis, found ready customers. The sale was thronged for the two days on which it was held, and finally brought in the magnificent sum of £1000 to swell the hospital's funds.

In those early days it was largely the generosity of the local nobility and gentry that enabled the Suffolk General to survive. The Marquis of Bristol and Sir William Parker of Melford contributed regularly and generously to its funds. The former wrote to the Committee in 1829, 'Nobody can feel more anxiety for the permanent prosperity of the Hospital than I do. No Institution . . . is more likely to give effectual relief and durable advantages to a large portion of the community.' There is no doubt, that, with all its imperfections, the old Suffolk General did exactly this!

THE GAS MEN

Gas came to Bury in 1834, not in 1824 as a succession of 19th-century directories and guidebooks would have it. The error is understandable, however, because there had been talk of gas coming to Bury from at least 1820 and probably earlier. It was in 1820 that, by an Act for Paving, Lighting, etc., it was made lawful for the Paving Commissioners 'to dig and sink trenches, to lay mains and pipes, to put stop-cocks or plugs (upon the same) with the consent of the owners or occupiers . . . and to do all other reasonable acts for conduct-ing gas or gas lights, for the purpose of lighting such streets, highways, lanes, squares, and public passages', and also 'to enter into any agreement . . . for supplying gas to any person . . . who shall be desirous to light . . . any house, shop, or other building.'

When application was made in 1833 for permission to lay down pipes for lighting with gas, the 'Bury and Norwich Post' stated that it would be a matter of regret, if any attempt, 'like so many preceding ones shall fail'. No doubt the opposition had been in part to do with the financial aspect of the undertaking. But there may have been a certain apprehension, too. As early as 1792 a Cornish house had been lighted by gas by the Scottish mechanic, William Murdoch, who then proceeded to introduce his marvellous new lighting into certain factories in the north of England. Nevertheless, in the 1820s the methods of installation and maintenance left much to be desired. A gas works inspector was appointed by the Secretary of State in 1821 because of 'the considerable apprehensions entertained of the consequence that would follow the explosion of the gasometer in a crowded neighbourhood.' This was surely enough to shake most people's confidence!

Not only that, but the eminent Sir William Congreve, appointed by the government to report on the gas light establishment of the metropolis in 1823, produced as a part of his findings the depressing fact that a gasometer of thirty thousand cubic feet capacity, when rendered explosive by a certain proportion of atmospheric air, would be equal to 62 barrels of gunpowder! That Congreve was rather obsessed by exploding gasometers is evident in the controversy aroused by his appointment as gas works inspector in 1824, when 'really scientific men' like Sir Humphrey Davy (so described in the House) said that Congreve talked nonsense. The latter persisted however in his mistrust and told hair-raising tales of how fires were lit close to gasometers in frosty weather and how gas was frequently floated in highly inflammable coal-tar instead of in water. Whether he was right or wrong, he must surely have done a certain amount of damage to the early gas industry.

Even the most enthusiastic advocates of gas lighting, though, could make statements which were far from reassuring. When the editor of the 'Bury and Norwich Post' wrote, in December 1824, that there was 'some prospect of this beautiful discovery being imported to the town of Bury' he, at the same time, quoted what purported to be a speech made to catch converts, which had been delivered at a recent meeting at the Stamford gas works. In it, references were made to recent accidents from gas in London, the reason for which had been, 'the hurried and unskilful manner in which the works had been executed, occasioning a constant leakage from the pipes'. The loss of gas in London, it was stated, would light a considerable town! Not only this, but old gun-barrels had been used for the earliest piping, and these were continually rusting away and causing accidents . . . the wonder is that the 'gas-men' were welcomed anywhere at all!

Come to Bury they did, however, in the persons of Messrs. Malam and Peckston. In February 1833, John Malam and Co. of Hull applied for permission to lay down pipes for lighting shops and private houses with the promise that, when required, they would also light the streets. According to the local paper there was 'a great desire amongst the inhabitants for the introduction of this beautiful light into the town.'

On March 6, 1833, Mr Thomas Snowden Peckston of St. Helier, Jersey, attended the meeting of the Paving Commis-

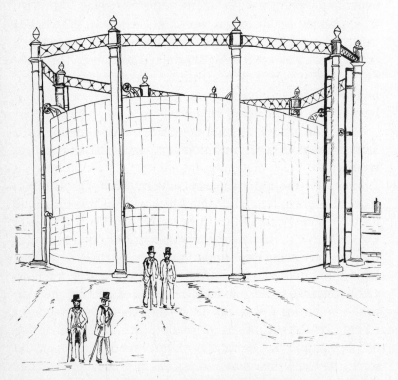

The 'Christening' of a Victorian gasometer. Bury Gasworks was built in Tayfen Road on a site once used for executing criminals. Up until the late 1870s gas was used mainly for lighting. To begin with it was burnt from unshielded burners. Then in 1878 Carl Auer von Welsbach invented the incandescent mantle, a revolutionary improvement.

138

sioners to make his final proposition on lighting the town with gas. It was agreed that Malam and Peckston should be allowed to lay down mains and pipes for lighting the houses and for a few lights in Abbeygate Street, engaging to light the whole of the town, whenever called upon, within the next 10 years.

Mr Peckston was described in the press as 'a person of scientific as well as practical acquaintance with the subject of gas', a man who had been involved with the gas-works of London, Dublin and many large towns. In fact he had been superintendent of the gas light works at St Helier, was a civil engineer and a half-pay purser in the Royal Navy. He had other interests in East Anglia, too, and was concerned with schemes at Lowestoft, Woodbridge, Bungay, Beccles and Stowmarket. In March 1833, he purchased a piece of ground at Tay Fen for the erection of the gas works, a site formerly used for the execution of criminals.

Mr Malam disappears early from the scene in the annals of Bury's gas-works. Mr Peckston held on to the lead, so to speak, until 1835, when a local syndicate, called the Bury St Edmunds Gas Light Company, bought the Bury gas works from Mr Peckston for £6,000 in cash and £6,000 in fully-paid shares in the company. By 1849, however, the unfortunate Mr Peckston was being described in legal documents as 'late of Fleet prison', where he had been confined for some time for debt. What became of him thereafter I have been unable to discover. It seems a sad epilogue to the story of the two men who brought 'that beautiful light' to the town.

THIS FINE SUBSTANTIAL BUILDING

How many of the customers who saunter through those shops on Cornhill that were formerly the Bury St Edmunds Public Library, are aware that this fine building was actually built as a Corn Exchange in 1836?

To read the newspapers of that period is to see the Borough taking its first tottering steps away from the rough and ready regime of the 18th century towards the Victorian era, with its social improvements and scientific innovations. There was talk of a railway being constructed between Bury and Ispwich. Gas-lighting had been recently introduced into the town. In February of 1836, the Borough Police Force was formed with Mr Richard Coney as Superintendent of four Day Policemen and six Night Police.

There was an abundance of crime arising mainly from the dire poverty in which a large section of the populace was compelled to exist. The sentences that were meted out were inordinately harsh. In March of that year, for example, David Balls, aged fifteen, was transported for seven years for breaking into a house and stealing a five-shilling piece and some bread and cheese. There was plain hooliganism to be curbed. Stone-throwing for instance, between gangs of young men and boys, who apparently assembled in the Churchyard for that purpose every lunchtime, to the hazards of passers-by and of invalids who walked beneath the trees.

For the better-off, of course, life was more gracious. They could stroll in the select precincts of the Botanic Gardens, or enjoy Italian operas at the theatre, while a section of them devoted their energies to running the Borough, and inaugurated improvements such as the New Corn Exchange.

The first plan submitted for the new building in April, 1836 was of a room, sixty feet by thirty-eight, attached to the south end of the Market Cross, and with a reading-room built on to the north end of the Cross. The Mayor was particularly enthusiastic about this design, and hoped they might eventually have a library added to the proposed reading-room.

In May, however, Councillor Peter Gedge, editor of the Bury and Norwich Post, submitted a plan which involved pulling down the Market Cross and building the Exchange on its site, re-using the old materials. By doing this he claimed they would save as much as £800, and would not have any problems about the new building not harmonising with the existing one. Fortunately, the following month a compromise was reached, and the final design was produced. In this the new building was detached by a space of thirty feet from the Cross and was lighted by a skylight in its centre. The architect was Mr Backhouse and the Markets Committee estimated that £1200, plus subscriptions from local landowners, would be sufficient to cover the cost.

There was to be more discord over the builders' contract, which was eventually given to the Stowmarket firm of Rednall & Co., to the indignation of Bury people who thought local builders should have been employed. Then in August came a demand for the Clerk of Works to inspect the building, as it was claimed soft bricks were being used in the interior. No doubt there were some red faces then for the Markets Committee had to admit that they had not been able to afford a Clerk of Works. Apparently, because of the soft state of the ground, the foundations had had to be dug to a depth of eight feet in places, and this had involved a lot of extra expense. By March 1837, however, the Exchange was finally erected and described in the 'Bury Post' as 'the greatest accommodation ever afforded to agriculturalists in this town'.

However, barely eleven years later, users were complaining that sometimes it was impossible for anyone in the Exchange to stir an inch, or to get in or out. Some sort of expansion was urgently needed, for the previous decade had seen the advent and the development of the railway-system and trains were bringing ever-increasing numbers of merchants to Bury on market days. It was decided therefore, to extend the building on the south side by thirty-nine feet, and to make two entrances on the east and west sides, with attached porticos and pediments. By August 1848 the work was completed and, according to the local press, 'merchants of large experience pronounce it to be one of the best rooms in England, possessing the advantages of light with protection from the weather'.

The extended Corn Exchange continued as such for the next fourteen years, when once again expansion of business made more space a necessity. It was found this time in the grandiose new building in Abbeygate Street, which we know today. So in October 1862, the age of the crinoline, when the American Civil War was raging, and the sewing-machine was a novelty, the 'old' Corn Exchange became the New Provision Market, thereby causing another short-lived furore in the town.

The building was, at this time, slightly modified in the interests of ventilation, all the blank windows being taken out, except those over the doors. There was accommodation for fourteen butchers as well as stalls for sellers of poultry, eggs and butter and for 'others'. It was the definition of this last category which caused trouble. Certain shopkeepers in the Buttermarket were very anxious to have all the market-stalls moved away from their doors and into the new hall. The market-traders naturally took a different view. They presented a petition to the council, stating that, 'We, the undersigned, stall-keepers, and others, having experienced considerable loss and disappointment by our removal from the old-established market-place, do most respectfully beg . . . to retain the places, that have been occupied by stall-keepers for generations past.' In the end it was agreed that the sellers of manufactured goods and the greengrocers might remain in the Buttermarket.

In 1899 the building adopted quite a new role and sallied forth into a more refined domain. For the major portion of it became the Borough's School of Art, the remainder of the accommodation being used, partly as a small provision-market, partly as a fire-station. At the opening ceremony the Mayor revealed that there had been many in favour of pulling down this 'fine substantial building'. Externally the building was now altered in appearance by the addition of a parapet and pediments round the windows, and the name of the

Bury St Edmunds Library, 1982. Corn-exchange. Provision market. School of Art. Fire Station. Public Reference Library. Free Library. Now a shopping precinct. There can be few other buildings in the town which have provided so many, and such varied public services.

school was placed, in raised stone letters, above the pillar-flanked classical doorway on the main street.

It was not until 1923 that the building first accommodated a library. This was the magnificent collection of books, bequeathed to the town by Mr Milner-Gibson Cullum, now housed in the Bury Record Office. It was housed on the ground floor hall, on the east side of the School of Art, and was a Public Reference Library, open on Thursday and Saturday afternoons and on Saturday evenings. When Bury Free Library was opened in May 1931 providing a lending-service for two hours, four evenings a week, it was housed in the Athenaeum. It moved from there to the Market Cross in 1936, and finally took over the former premises of the Art School in 1937. There it remained for forty-five years, until moving to its present luxurious home in St Andrew's Street.

Now the old building, its face once again having been discreetly lifted, accommodates vendors and welcomes purchasers. Coins clink merrily. The wheel has turned full circle.

A GIRL CALLED LOUISE

At the junction of Horringer Road and Vinery Road in Bury, there is an unusual monument, originally designed to incorporate a drinking trough for horses and dogs. I must admit to having passed it countless times before curiosity impelled me one day to inspect it more closely and to discover that it was, in fact, the memorial to Ouida, the Victorian novelist, who had been born a few hundred yards away in Hospital Road. Further investigation revealed that the erection of the memorial, which was unveiled on a pleasant November day in 1908, had been a national, rather than a local event. For the funds for it had been raised by the 'Daily Mirror', who in company with the 'Daily Mail' had re-discovered the elderly, ailing, and impoverished writer, when she was dragging out the last wretched years of her existence in Viareggio in Italy. Indeed it was suggested that the 'Mirror' was making amends for having incensed and humiliated Ouida in the last year of her life, by printing a photograph, purporting to be of her, but which was actually of an aged and pathetic-looking Italian peasant woman.

However it was, on that November day several thousands are said to have arrived from all over the country to pay tribute to the woman, who had been in her heyday, the most popular novelist of her age. The Mayor and the Council walked from the centre of the town in procession. Lady Evelyn Guinness motored over from Elveden Hall to unveil the memorial. Mr Bannister of the 'Daily Mirror' made a speech explaining the significance of the bronze figures on the monument as aspects of Ouida's character. The girl caressing a dog symbolised Sympathy. The figure brandishing a sword depicted Courage. He spoke at length on Ouida's great love of animals, particularly of dogs. Alderman Clarke, on the other hand, spoke mainly of Ouida's novels, quoting extensively from the laudatory letter which had been published in the local press by another Victorian novelist, who had adopted the pseudonym 'Rita'.

It appears to have been a dignified and pleasant ceremony. And yet it had its incongruous side, too. For, despite the efforts of Mr Gery Milner-Gibson Cullum of Hardwick House, who had befriended Ouida in her latter years, the folk of Bury had made but a paltry contribution to the monument. Which is, perhaps, not to be wondered at, since Ouida, who had spent her first eighteen years in Bury, had on more than one occasion made it clear that she felt nothing but contempt and dislike for the town. A town which she had described in her short story, 'Blue and Yellow' as 'that slowest and dreariest of boroughs, where the streets are as full of grass as an acre of pasture land.' Indeed in 1907, when a plaque had been affixed to her birthplace, she had written to Mr Gery Milner-Gibson Cullum, 'This tomfoolery in Suffolk annoys me very much. I identify myself with my father's French race and blood, and I shall be greatly obliged if you would do your best to prevent any inscription of the kind you named being put as you say.'

What manner of woman was she, then, this reluctant daughter of our town? Her biographers tell us of a gifted, eccentric, impossible woman, whose reputation, sadly, was founded on her first, immature novels. These were devoured by an avid public forever craving more, and can be compared, perhaps, to our own television 'soap-operas'. They were the products of an overgrown schoolgirl's wild imagination, and today a novel like 'Held In Bondage', published in 1863, can only seem absurd, with its aristocratic, cardboard characters, its ridiculous plot, and total lack of realism. That Ouida had

146

been remembered for such novels, and not for the work of her mature years, where she can, on occasion, rival Oscar Wilde for wit, and Zola for realistic social commentary, this is surely her great tragedy!

Nor was Ouida's professional reputation helped by her personality. She was a plain, if not an ugly, little woman with a raucous voice. Her flamboyant, unrequited passions made her a laughing-stock on more than one occasion. She was rude, self-opinionated, extremely conceited and highly eccentric. In her later years she lavished all her affections on the dozens of dogs she kept in her Italian villa. Not a woman whom her public could take seriously, it seemed. Yet in works like her critical essays she reveals a first-class intellect which could express itself in lucid and elegant prose.

It was not Ouida, the novelist, though, whom Bury knew in the 1840s and 50s. For then she was plain Louise Ramé. Her background has always been something of a mystery, partly because Ouida, herself, fabricated deliberate untruths about it, partly because commentators and biographers have been guilty of inaccuracies, that have confused the issue even more. What is certain is that her mother was a Susan Sutton, who was born in Bury in 1813, and was the youngest of three sisters.

Susan's father, William Sutton, was described on her baptismal certificate as a merchant's clerk. Her eldest sister, Maria, twelve years older than Susan, married William B. Lockwood, a wine merchant, in 1823 and had four children by him before she died in 1831. William Lockwood then married the second Sutton sister, Mary Anne, who gave him a daughter. The Lockwoods were a well-known Bury family, and William's three brothers were all clerics. On January 16, 1838, Susan Sutton married Louis Ramé and the following announcement appeared in the 'Bury and Norwich Post' on January the 17th. 'Yesterday (Tuesday) at St Mary's Church in this town by the Rev. C. B. Lockwood, Louis Ramé, Esq., of L'Orient, to Susan, daughter of Mrs Sutton of West Terrace.'

The marriage-entry in St Mary's register describes Louis Ramé as a 'widower' and a 'gentleman' and gives his fathers occupation as a 'sailor', (not a 'tailor', as one biographer has erroneously transcribed it). Whatever Ramé was, (and it is obvious that his was not the aristocratic background, that Ouida later invented for him), he was not the conventional, middle-class husband, whom one would have expected Susan Sutton to have married. He was said to have taught French in Bury schools, which may have been the case. What is certain is that, after his marriage, he spent less and less time in Bury, and that little Louise was born and reared in her grand-

The Ouida Memorial. Ouida merits around three hundrd words in the *Oxford Companion to English Literature*. Yet her memorial is in an out-of-the-way corner, on the fringe of the town, unsignposted, and hard to track down.

148

mother's home in Union Terrace, almost like a fatherless child. According to her childhood journal, from which all her biographers have drawn extensively, Ouida nevertheless worshipped the father, who arrived from France at irregular intervals and filled his daughter's head with romantic tales of the noble circles in which he moved, and with his liberal, political views. That he did have connections with influential members of French society is borne out by the fact that he took Susan and his eleven-year-old daughter to Boulogne in 1850, where they visited the Princess Laetitia Bonaparte, and enjoyed the company of several upper-class French families. It has been suggested that Ramé was an agent for Louis Napoleon. I think that the late Janet Hitchman was probably correct in her assumption that he was a bigamist. For Ouida's first melodramatic novel, 'Held In Bondage', was basically a diatribe against the divorce-laws of the time, the story of two men who were trapped in wretched marriages. Moreover, when the novel was reprinted, Ouida apologised in a preface for its gaucheries and immaturity, but stressed the fact that she still felt as strongly about the novel's basic theme, and therefore had agreed to its being reissued.

From the young Louise's own accounts, her early childhood years were happy ones, in a comfortable middle-class home, with her Lockwood cousins for company. There were constant visitors, outings and parties, such as those given by Dr Hake in Guildhall Street for his daughter Lucy, who was five years Louise's junior. By the time Louise was ten, her Lockwood cousins were quite grown up, Maria, the eldest, being twenty-six, and Marianne, the youngest, fifteen. They seem to have spoiled their little cousin, and it was from Maria, that she acquired the name, which was to become world-famous. For 'Ouida' was only Louise's infantile way of pronouncing her own name, and Maria invented the spelling of it.

Why the young Louise suddenly became so disenchanted

with Bury is not clear. Was it just the frustration of a restless nature, which needed more stimulus, than that offered by a country market town? Or was it, as has been suggested, that Mr Ramé had become the target of sinister and unpleasant gossip? Whatever the reason, no-one was happier than eighteen year old Louise to leave her home town for London in 1857, never to return. One cannot help but wonder what Ouida's rasping tongue would have said about the decision to commemorate her in the birthplace, which she had endeavoured to ignore and to forget!

OFF THE RAILS

It was a foreigner from Norfolk who told me to go and look at Bury St Edmunds railway-station.

'But I've seen it,' I protested, 'Thousands of times!'

'With half an eye, I bet!' he said scornfully. 'I want you to look at it. Go down there on a Sunday morning. Stand and gaze a bit. The building's a treasure.'

I found he was right.

Opened in 1847, the station was designed by Sancton Wood, (although it is sometimes mistakenly attributed to Frederick Barnes). At first glance it may look a trifle fanciful with its pair of domed towers and a gabled stationhouse, that has been compared to a Cambridge master's lodge. Soon, however, the harmony of the whole concept becomes evident, and we see a building which is aesthetically satisfying. Our Victorian townsfolk were certainly proud of it. In the local paper it was referred to as 'one of the most commodious and finest stations in the kingdom.' Then, of course, it was in all its pristine glory with new red-and-white bricks, handsome stone staircases, and shining brass fittings in that noble room which was the pay-office.

Oddly enough the opening of the station building itself was somewhat of an anti-climax. This was because the ceremony to mark the arrival of the railway in the town had taken place almost a year beforehand, on December 7, 1846. The weather was terrible, but nothing could damp the ardour of the crowds who flocked down to Northgate Street to participate in the celebrations. It was a momentous event for them. The days of frustratingly slow road-travel were behind them. A whole new world was opening up.

In 1846 the trains which steamed into the temporary station at Bury (on the east side of Northgate Street) were owned by the Bury and Ipswich Railway Company, which was closely connected to the Eastern Union Company, with which it was to amalgamate the following year. Its chairman was John Chevallier Cobbold, Esquire, of Ipswich, who had probably done more than any other person to bring the railway into the region.

On this December day in 1846 a special train had started from Shoreditch to pick up the Ipswich V.I.Ps. It left Ipswich for Bury with two engines, twenty carriages, and between three hundred and four hundred passengers. There were two elegant saloons for the Directors and other officers of the Company. At all the stations along the route, most of them only partially completed, triumphal arches had been erected. At Stowmarket there was also a special gallery for lady spectators, and half a cask of beer for the labourers. Flags, flowers and arches adorned Haughley, Elmswell, and Thurston stations. At around two-thirty the train pulled into the temporary station at Bury, having taken one hour and forty-five minutes to cover the twenty-six miles.

Meanwhile the Mayor, Council, and principal tradesmen of Bury had been marching from the town centre to Northgate Street with a band playing and flags flying. When they had greeted their guests, they all returned in procession to the Angel, and later went up to the Concert Room, our present Art Gallery, where three hundred sat down to a luxurious champagne dinner. A banner behind the top table proclaimed, 'Success to Agriculture and Commerce . . . Ipswich and Bury Railway.' There were some remarkably poetical speeches. The Recorder compared the coming of the railway to Bury to that of a bride-groom coming to his bride, 'laden with presents' and foretold an imminent Golden Age of prosperity for the town. Mr Cobbold waxed lyrical about his

152

schooldays in Bury, then made the point that he would much have preferred to have travelled home in the holidays in a train, rather than in the tardy coaches of his day. It was nine o'clock when the guests finally set off on their return journey to a display of fireworks and more music from the band.

The sentiments of one Bury citizen concerning the arrival of the railway can be seen in a letter, written by William Bodham Donne, the critic and scholar who lived next to the theatre in Westgate Street, to his friend, Bernard Barton, the Quaker poet of Woodbridge. 'The passenger-trains open on Monday, and come as early as you can, as the accidents usually begin about ten days after the opening,' he advised. He then went on, 'I had one devoted friend, who came from Ipswich by the first luggage train some three weeks ago. He was four hours on his journey of twenty-six miles, and though he rode with the stokers and was blackened by the smoke, was well-nigh frozen when he arrived.'

At this period railway accidents were frequent, and there were weekly lists of reports of them in the press. Even as late as 1865 the pressure-group which was advocating the provision of some sort of communication cord, could cite as common occurences, axles breaking, tyres coming off wheels and carriages catching fire and running off the rails. One accident, which occurred in 1850 had a special relevance for Bury, as it concerned their own station-master.

The sequence of events which ended in catastrophe started at Bury station on the morning of the fourth of October, when a tube burst in the engine of the Bury to Ipswich train. There was no pilot engine at Bury, and it would have taken from two to three hours to get up sufficient steam to start one of the ordinary engines. Gideon Hatchwell, the Bury stationmaster, (thirty-four years old and a father of four) acted in what he obviously thought was the best interests of his passengers. He knew that if the train from Bury did not appear, the engine going to Norwich from Haughley Junction would come along

153

the line looking for it. He therefore called in four of the Company's horses to pull the two carriages along the track towards Haughley. He himself climbed on to some luggage on top of the leading carriage, while his porter did likewise on the second carriage. This was apparently so that he would see the other engine as soon as it came into view. Before they started, he sent a communication to the General Manager explaining what he was about to do and his reasons for doing it.

To begin with all went well, and doubtless the passengers were happy to be on the move. They arrived at Thurston without incident, but at this point the Thurston station-master, thirty-three year old James Walton decided, for some reason, to join Hatchwell. His action was never satisfactorily explained. His assistance was apparently not needed, and except in a dire emergency, a stationmaster was forbidden to leave his station. Riding on top of carriages was also expressly forbidden. Was it that he just succumbed to the temptation of a joy-ride? Whatever the reason, he had taken a fateful step. They met the engine from Haughley as they arrived at the second bridge after Thurston station. The horses were dis-missed and the engine attached. There was now to need for any 'look-outs' on top of the carriages. But as the train set off again towards Ipswich, gathering speed until it was travelling at around fifteen miles per hour, the three railway employees remained where they were. The two stationmasters, sitting together with their backs to the engine, were so high up that their heads were well above the engine-chimney.

They passed a third bridge. Then as the fourth bridge, Jennings Bridge, approached, the porter, who sat facing the stationmasters, saw to his horror that this one was much lower than the other bridges. Tragedy struck before he could do anything to avert it. The heads of the two men hit the arch with such force that pieces of brick were dislodged from it. Gideon Hatchwell was knocked from the roof, but James

Walton still lay on it, face upwards. The screams of the porter and passengers alerted the driver. The engine was stopped. But neither of them could be helped. Hatchwell, his head horribly mutilated, was breathing his last, while Walton was already dead. The bodies were carried back to Thurston Station.

At the inquest the attitude of the authorities was unsympathetic. The porter, the only available scapegoat, was sacked, the two stationmasters censured. No-one will ever know what incited two mature men in responsible jobs to commit a blatantly foolish act that lost them their lives.

Bury Railway Station c. 1850. The opening of the railway between Bury and Ipswich in 1846 had many and varied effects on the life of the town. For example a larger Corn Exchange had to be built to accommodate the new influx of merchants. And Station omnibuses became a familiar sight in front of the town's hotels.

BICYCLES AND BALLOONS

For the athletic and energetic Bury St Edmunds provides a wealth of sporting facilities. Rugby. Football. Cricket. Swimming. Basketball. Badminton. Tennis. They all have their adherents and for many the Leisure Centre and the Victory Sports Ground are twin meccas. Nor is the local taste for sport a recently acquired one. In 1886, according to an entertaining compilation entitled, 'Twelve Months' Pleasure in Bury,' there were thirty six days of cricket, sixteen football-matches, a hundred miles of bicycle races and eleven rifle-shooting contests.

In the late 19th century, bicycling was enjoying a tremendous boom. In the 1890s there were at least two major clubs in the town. A bicycle Club Ball was held annually at the Athenaeum and the Bicycle and Athletic Club Sports was an important annual event on the local sporting calendar. On April 11, 1898, these were held on Easter Monday on the Cricket Field in Cemetery Road, now Kings Road, in surprisingly good weather for the time of year. There was a record gate which brought in over £30. The Band of the 2nd Volunteer Battalion of the Suffolk Regiment played to an appreciative crowd. Mrs E. W. Lake presented some handsome prizes, an Ensign Bicycle being given to the winner of the 2 Miles Cycle Handicap, whilst the other winners received a dressing-case, a clock, a teapot, silver candlesticks, and a watch and chain. I wonder how many of these hard-won trophies are still proudly treasured in Bury homes today.

The town's sporting tastes, however, were not always the comparatively refined ones of the past hundred years. Back in the 18th and early 19th centuries cock-fighting was probably the most popular spectator-sport in this country and Bury's tastes followed suit. This barbaric business was often associated with public-houses and we find notices in the 'Suffolk Mercury' in the 1740s advertising 'mains', as the fights were called, at the 'Spreadeagle' in Bury, and at Thomas Williamson's at the Toll-Gate. In November, 1746, the latter house was the scene of an important main between the Gentlemen of Mildenhall and the Gentlemen of Bury.

There were other kinds of sport, to be found in Bury's 18th century inns, of course. Singing for prizes of gloves was one of the more innocuous and less strenuous. More exciting,

Mr Poole's ascent in October 1785. The first balloon ascent in Great Britain had been made only fourteen months previously by James Tytler in Edinburgh. The first sea-crossing had taken place in January, 1785, when Jeffries and Blanchard crossed from Dover to Calais. Thus Mr Poole's ascent was regarded as a landmark in Bury's history.

157

however, was the kind of match held in November, 1725 at the Half-Moon Inn in the Buttermarket. This was a 'Tryal of Skill' at back sword, sword and dagger, sword and buckler, and quarter staff, between Richard Jones of Denbigh and James Harris of London, the latter intriguingly described as 'the oldest swordsman in England.' As a subsidiary entertainment, six pairs of gloves were to be played for at cudgels, the rules of this match being simply, 'he who breaks a head wins a point'.

Those of our townsmen who kept their heads intact could at this era enjoy the thrills of the turf, for there was a Bury Course, the location of which puzzles local historians today. Bury Races were obviously notable occasions, because in May, 1725, Powells Puppet Show arrived in town 'to divert the Quality and Gentry with new entertainments every evening during the Horse-Race, concluding before the evening Assemblies began.'

As bicycling was the craze of the 1880s and 1890s, so was ballooning of the 1780s and 90s. In November, 1783 the blue and gold balloon built by the brothers Montgolfier had ascended from the Bois de Boulogne, enabling Jean Pilatre de Rozier and the Marquis d'Arlandes to become the worlds first true aeronauts. Thus when Mr Poole went up in a balloon from Bury in October, 1785, the sport was still a novelty and attracted a huge audience. The event, obviously regarded as a landmark in Bury's history, was reported in great detail in the 'Bury and Norwich Post', where local news at this period was normally very briefly reported.

The gentry assembled by noon of the great Saturday to watch the balloon being filled, the 'intrepid aeronaut' meanwhile showing what was regarded as an astonishing sang-froid. He was still collected and composed when he climbed into the car and prepared to ascend. However two 'wings' or sails, with which he was experimenting as an aid to steering, proved more of a hindrance than a help and had to be cut off.

When he did finally leave terra firma, Mr Poole ascended with a rapidity that sent the thousands down below him into raptures. To this he responded magnificently by taking off his hat and waving his flag for as long as they could see him. Mr Poole's reported description of the ascent is a fascinating one. He described the various sensations he experienced. His pleasure in the beautiful sky. His ascent through snowy-topped clouds. The intense cold. The deep silence when he could clearly hear the watch beating in his pocket. The unpleasant sensation in his ears. He finally made a perfect landing at Earl Soham, having travelled twenty-eight miles in an hour and eleven minutes, which by 18th century standards must have seemed miraculous.

Mr Poole's return to Bury at midnight in a post-chaise-and-four, with the car and balloon on the roof, was an occasion for almost hysterical rejoicing, since it had been feared that he had been blown out to sea. The horses were unfastened from the chaise and the exultant crowd drew Mr Poole around the Market Cross no less than three times. Fireworks were then let off, the display lasting until two o'clock on Sunday morning, by which time the revelry got sadly out of hand.

No doubt a wonderful time was had by all. All, that is, except the entrepreneur who had organised the event. Poor man. The locals who had flocked to the spectacle, avid for entertainment, had eschewed his viewing-enclosure and its admission tickets. Instead they had climbed into, and on top of, all the neighbouring buildings at no charge at all. The organiser's takings did not even defray his expenses – or so he complained. Such were the hazards of the sporting-life in the 18th century.

THE GREAT FLOOD

When you read this, the sun may be blazing down from a blue sky. On the other hand it may be raining. And not just in a half-hearted, drizzly fashion, but in a steady, drumming downpour, that elicits groans and moans from the most long-suffering of us, and comments to the effect, that we've never known such weather. We have, of course, if we are British. So have our parents. And our grandparents. And our great-grandparents. Yet whenever it happens to us, we still manage to be surprised and outraged. And very often we are as unprepared as were the good folk in Bury St Edmunds on July 21 and 22, 1879.

1879 had been a wretched year. It had been intensely cold and dry to begin with. Then from April to September there had been almost continuous rain. From reports in the newspapers one can visualise the whole population of the British Isles becoming more and more depressed. There had been virtually no spring. Now summer was turning into a procession of cool, gloomy days. So the people of Bury were doubtless looking forward to the Annual Gala of the United Friendly Societies, which was to be held in the Botanic Gardens on the 21st of July. All the usual attractions were to be there. Itinerant entertainers of all kinds. Steam roundabouts. Sanger's Waxworks. Refreshment-booths. Fireworks. And an opportunity to see the wonders of electric lighting. The preceding week had brought three fine days. No doubt this engendered optimism in the hearts of the townsfolk.

But on Saturday, July 19, the rain returned. On Sunday

there were torrential cloudbursts, and by Monday morning it was obvious that the River Lark would burst its banks if the rain continued much longer and it certainly showed no signs of easing off. Nevertheless people came to the Gala in their hundreds, tramping the meadowland into a quagmire in their search for some entertainment on that wretched wet day. Not that there was much to be had. Most of the stall-holders had conceded victory to the elements by early afternoon, for the water was already beginning to creep over the lowest ground. There was a poor display of fireworks. The electric light made the scene more desolate, if anything. The stallkeepers and showmen must have retired to their beds that night with heavy hearts, for the usually profitable Gala had been literally a wash-out.

For two of those stallkeepers there was to be a rude awakening the following morning. These were James Westrope of Bury, a vendor of confectionery and Alfred Cook of London, who sold fancy wares. Their caravans were in a group parked beneath some old elm-trees in the north-west corner of the meadow. Just after four o'clock one of the largest of the trees suddenly toppled, its roots having been loosened by the water, and fell directly on to the two vans occupied by Westrope and Cook. Cook's caravan ended up between two of the chief limbs of the tree, a branch having fallen through on to the bed on which he and his wife were sleeping. Westrope's van was so damaged that the floor, and part of his bed, had to be sawn through, before he could eventually be dragged clear. Incredibly only Alfred Cook was injured in the mishap, and that slightly.

The sightseers, who came thronging to the Gardens later that morning to see the two wrecked caravans, and to start subscription-lists to help the two showmen, witnessed an unforgettable spectacle. The show-people had really been caught out by the floods. In the refreshment booths the water was level with the tables. Sanger's Waxwork Exhibition was

161

flooded up to the floors of the caravans. The steam engine, which was immersed to above the tops of its wheels, was being hauled out of the mud by three horses and a gang of strong men, pulling on a wire rope. Sanger's vans were eventually moved by the same method, the last one being hauled away just before another huge elm-tree came crashing to the ground. The caravans were taken up to Angel Hill and Mustow Street, while the waters gradually subsided, leaving behind them a waste of mud. But it was not only the show-people, who were having their problems, that Tuesday morning. Eastgate Street was flooded to some distance north and south of the Abbot's Bridge, which was blocked by detritus, forming a dam. The fronts of the houses had to be banked up with clay and pedestrians made their way along the flooded road on planks, which were raised to a height of over a foot on stone 'pillars'. Despite precautions, houses and shops were flooded.

The Annual Gala of the United Friendly Societies was held in the Botanic Gardens, (today's Abbey Gardens) on Monday, July 21, 1879. It had rained on the Saturday. There were cloudbursts on Sunday. Monday was a wretched wet day which culminated in the Lark's bursting its banks. By Tuesday morning the Gardens resembled a giant lake.

162

The Fox Inn suffered badly. So did Elam's, the baker's.

Other districts of the town were also under water. Raingate Street, Maynewater Lane, the Butts, and the Spread Eagle area were most affected. An eyewitness described the scene at the bottom of Friar's Lane as looking 'like a great lake, with trees and the tops of gates, fences, and haycocks, rising out of it.'

On the fringe of the town, market-gardeners and farmers suffered serious damage. John Barrett, one of the largest florists and fruiterers, had more than half of his premises inundated. The water had rushed into his greenhouses. His strawberry beds were completely covered and the whole crop lost. The heads of his plantations of flowers could just be seen peeping above the water.

For long after, this holiday week-end was referred to by local people as 'the time of the Great Flood'. Of course, there have been other great floods in the town's history. Another occasion when the townsfolk had to battle to keep their chins above water was in August, 1829, in the Stamford Bridge area. Then the heavily swollen river was carrying quantities of oats through the arches of the bridge. In an attempt to prevent this, hurdles were put down into the water. Inevitably the river was raised to such an extent that one of the arches was 'blown up', doubtless a costly mishap. And most towns-folk have vivid memories of that Monday in September, 1968, when around three hundred homes were flooded in Bury, after more than three inches of rain had fallen in twenty-four hours. The scene must have been very similar to that of 1879, with the lower part of the Abbey Gardens under water, and the flood spreading along Eastgate Street and Mustow Street. Maynewater Lane, Raingate Street and the Spread Eagle suffered just as badly as they had almost a century before. There was no electricity supply that day, and cars were of less use than horses and carts were in 1879.

A VICTORIAN WALKS TO FORNHAM

I remember, during my first year of teaching in a Glasgow secondary school, embarking with enthusiasm on a local-history project. I took my class out one afternoon to visit the site of what had been a Victorian tea-garden on the riverside, a pleasant place of resort for the wealthy city merchants on holiday afternoons. The baffled expression in the eyes of my pupils stays with me until this day. We stood there in a Glasgow drizzle, in one of the most depressed (and depressing) areas of the city, surrounded by decaying tenement blocks, with an unlovely stretch of dockside as a backdrop, and suffered a communal and total failure of imagination. Not a blade of grass, not a tree remained of the pretty scene we had admired in our history book. It might have come from another country.

How different the case for the fortunate schoolchildren of Bury, I think, as I watch them working enthusiastically in the Record Office. How comparatively little they need stretch their imaginations came home to me recently, when I came across a series of *Guided Walks*, in the 'Bury and Norwich Post' of 1886. Of course the town and its environs have changed since then, but what surprises us is not what has gone, but what remains.

One walk began in Westgate Street in the neighbourhood of St Peter's Church which was then a mere twenty eight years old, having been built in 1858 in Victorian Gothic style, with a spire, which (though looking rather alien to Suffolk) was much admired. Beyond it was the Suffolk General Hospital, (today a residential home) with its spacious gardens, or 'airing-ground', stretching between Hospital Road and West-

164

gate Road. The Spread Eagle Inn stood, as it does today, near the junction of Horringer Road and Hardwick Lane. There was no Vinery Road, but the 'pleasant villa residence' known as The Vinery stood high on the rising ground, and was the residence of a Colonel Byron, Commandant of the Depot 12th Regiment. Walking on up Horringer Road there were many pretty allotment gardens to admire and, at the top, the imposing West Mill.

Horringer Red House, and especially its garden, were described in great detail, obviously because of the achievement of its owner, the Reverend R. S. Fox in transforming what had been chalk and stone pits, with their accompanying débris, into a fairytale landscape of 'hills and dells, steep inclines, rustic steps, formidable precipices and yawning caverns'. (Mr Fox's success was attributed to his acquaintance with Alpine scenery.)

Of Horringer itself our roving reporter declared that it would be difficult to find a pleasanter and prettier village. Beautifully wooded, it was surrounded with fertile fields and contained fine residences, such as the handsome Brooke House, Hopleys, and Horringer House, the latter famed for its large oaks.

The route back to Bury led through Westley and along the Newmarket Road past the Barracks, which had a frontage of 250 yards, and covered an area of twenty acres in all. Beyond them were the extensive excavations of the long-disused, chalk-and-clay pits, known as St Peter's Pits. Our guide gave his imagination full rein when his eye lit on these. He saw the 'romantic and irregular spot' transformed into a public garden or park, the gift, perhaps, of some second Jankyn Smyth with aesthetic ideas and 'a long purse'.

The aim of the *Guided Walks* being to show tourists what Bury had to offer in the way of the antique and the picturesque, it is not surprising that much wordage on another walk was devoted to a battle.

Starting in Northgate Street this time our guide fairly trotted along the first section of the course in order to spend a considerable time gloating over the site of the Battle of Fornham. He did mention the old Grammar School (which we can still see today), the ruins of St Saviour's Hospital, and the new Wesleyan Middle Class Boys' School (later to become Culford School) in Thing-Hoo Road. Wasn't he happy, though, when he had passed the Tollgate Inn and could look down on those low-lying meadows on either side of the Lark, where a piece of English history was made. He had to tell his readers the whole story, which, as it happens, was rather an exciting one.

It began with the family problems of Henry II, whose wife and sons had taken up arms against him. One of their supporters was the Earl of Leicester, who in 1173 was sent by the unsuspecting King over to Flanders. Here he proceeded to enlist the help of the Count of Flanders and the King of France on the side of the English rebels. On Michaelmas Day he landed near Walton Castle with a large band of Flemish mercenaries and was promptly given assistance by Hugh Bigod, Earl of Norfolk and Suffolk, who harboured him, with his Countess and his army, in Framlingham Castle.

From Framlingham, Leicester and his men sallied out to commit whatever mischief they could. They tried to take Dunwich. They razed Haughley Castle to the ground. Being wooden, it apparently made a fine bonfire. Such exploits, of course, were bound to come to the ears of the King eventually. When they did, two of the ablest royal militarists were summoned to put Leicester in his place. These were Humphrey de Bohun, who had been fighting Scots in faraway Lothian, and De Lucy, Lord Chief Justice of England.

We are told that when the Bigods, husband and wife, and especially the latter, heard of the royal army arriving in Bury, they literally gave their guests their marching orders. Leicester had no alternative but to march towards his Midlands home. By-passing Bury, he and his mercenaries made for the ford at Fornham St Genevieve and found themselves faced by the Royal Cavalry under de Bohun. The Flemish infantrymen were no match for the horsemen of England. There was slaughter, rout, and the Countess lost her jewellery. According to some accounts she threw it away because it was so heavy. Others say she was trying to hide it. At least one gold ring with a ruby on it has been found on the site. The Countess was finally captured. So was her traitorous husband. They

St Peter's Church. Built in 1858 to seat 450 people, it is a Victorian Gothic Church. Norman Scarfe praises it for displaying an 'admirable appreciation of local building materials'. (*Suffolk. A Shell Guide.*)

were both incarcerated in a Norman prison for quite some time.

The 1886 article told of a sword, spearheads, and a gold chain being found on the site. It was not until 1933, however, that the remarkable iron sword of Fornham Park was found in a ditch. Made in the twelfth century, it is three-and-a-half feet long, with an inscription inlaid in silver on the blade. On one side it reads 'I Nomine Deum'. On the reverse, 'Sanctus (abbreviated) Benedictus'. From whose hand, one wonders, could it have fallen? Perhaps from one of the skeletons found in the 1840s, when a large tree blew down in Fornham Park to reveal a grisly collection arranged with their heads lying close to the tree-trunk. In 1886 that discovery was fresh in people's minds.

No wonder, when the twelfth century sometimes seems to creep so close, that a mere hundred years seems no time at all! And isn't it something of a miracle, in this rapidly changing world, to be able to look at and enjoy the unchanged scene in and around the town of Bury?

THE SILVER SCREEN

The competition in the early days of cinematography must have been fierce. Ronald Bates, who had an electrical-engineering business in Abbeygate Street, figures largely in Bury's story. In 1908, for instance, whenever the Hippodrome (what we would term 'a variety-show') came to the Theatre Royal, Bates & Co. showed their 'animated pictures'. At a meeting of the Town Council in January, 1908 it was agreed by the Electrical Supply Committee to grant Bates & Co. a supply of current for use with an animatograph. The engineer had tested the apparatus and declared that if it were operated with care, it would not cause undue fluctuations of pressure. There was a stipulation, though, that the apparatus had to be skilfully manipulated and that the Corporation reserved the right to cut off its supply of current, should it interfere with the private lighting in the town!

A rival to Mr Bates made his appearance in 1909 in the formidable personage of Charles Thurston, the Norwich showman, renowned then for his 'Royal Show' of animated pictures, and one of the leading exponents of cinematography in the region. In the 'Bury Post' of January 15, 1909, there is an advertisement for Thurston's Grand Picture Palace in St John's Street and its programme of 'Living Pictures of the Terrible Italian Earthquake.' In the 'Post' of January the 22nd there is a more intriguing advert. In addition to the animated pictures, Mr Thurston advertised a 'Great Beauty Show' at his Picture Palace, the first prize being a Ladies Cycle, 1909 Model. 'Come and See The Handsomest Ladies In Bury!' the readers were encouraged . . . But the rest, I'm afraid, is silence! No results of the great contest. No more adverts for Thurston's Picture Palace. One can only guess that Mr Thurston's publicity-stunt had been a shade too daring for Edwardian Bury. He wasn't mentioned again in the local papers until May, 1909 when he brought his Electric Vaudeville to D. W. Taylor's grounds near the Railway Station.

Meanwhile on March 12, 1909, the Anglo-American Picture and Variety Company, managed by A. E. Priest, combined animated pictures and variety acts in the Constitutional Hall in Guildhall Street. This hall was regularly advertised for hiring, and was described as seating up to 300 and being lighted throughout with electricity. On March 20, the hall was hired by Bates & Co for their 'Electric Pictures' and on April 9 they showed there moving pictures of the St Edmundsbury Pageant, which was a great local attraction. There are some accounts belonging to Bates & Co, in Bury Record Office, and we can see that at these early performances no great profits were made. Not when the money taken at the door amounted to £5-4s, the hire of the hall cost £2-5s., and the doorman, the sandwich-man and the fireman had all to be paid!

By January, 1911, Mr Bates was also active in St John's Street. In the 'Bury Free Press' of January 14, there is an account of a new Electric Theatre shortly to be opened there. Alterations to existing premises, (was this Thurston's Picture Palace?) were going on apace. There were to be seats for 250, half of which were tip-ups and the other half comfortably upholstered forms with backs. Only the best class of pictures was to be shown by Messrs. Bates. By the 28th of January more information was available. The novelty of having a continuous performance was made much of. The safety aspect was stressed. Fire was understandably the omnipresent dread. The public, in this instance, were assured that the machine had been erected in an iron box which stood behind a

170

brick wall at the further end of the hall. The pictures were shown through a slot in the wall, and the machine was in quite a separate building to the spectators. There was a second slot, through which the operator might look, and the reels of film were enclosed in steel cases. Of the four exits, two opening on to St John's Street were six feet wide and the two others were seven feet wide. Electric lighting was supplemented by gas. Ventilation was from a top skylight. The decor was in two shades of green. Admission prices ranged from twopence to sixpence.

The Electric Theatre vanished many years ago. According to one of the adverts in the early papers it was down at the

The Focus Cinema, 1982. Most residents of Bury still remember this cinema as the 'Odeon'. It presented to Brentgovel Street the uncompromising Face of the Thirties. The unsympathetic saw no merit in the building. For others the place was a worthy monument to the pre-war era.

bottom of St John's Street opposite a livery-stables. One feels there ought to be a plaque there to say that this was the spot where happiness was purchased for a modest fee.

Fire put an end to another of the town's early cinemas. This was the New Empire, which had opened in 1911 next door to the Post Office on Cornhill. At five-thirty a.m. on the morning of January 9, 1926, Mr Mears, a postman, heard loud cracking sounds coming from inside the cinema. Closer investigation revealed that the building was on fire. Despite the strenuous efforts of the fire-brigade, by daylight it had burned to the ground. A cigarette was deduced to have been the cause of the blaze. The ruins were viewed by crowds of disconsolate youngsters, who were bitterly upset because they were unable to see the final episode of a very popular serial-film called 'Galloping Horses.'

The first lessee of the Empire had been Mr S. E. Frank, one of Bury's cinema pioneers. In 1912 he was also manager and lessee of what was then known as the Gem Electric Theatre in St John's Street.

The Central, seating 650, opened in 1924 with an imposing half-page advertisement in the local papers, vaunting its palm-adorned entrance hall, thick pile carpeting and rich corded-velvet seats. With the projector at the rear of the screen it claimed to be silent, clean, draught-free and fully ventilated. It also claimed to be fireproof. As it turned out, however, it too was to be badly damaged by fire in September, 1930. Fortunately the blaze started after the cinema had emptied. Two patrolling policemen saw smoke and a flicker of flames just after midnight. Although the fire-brigade had everything under control by one a.m., the vestibule, the west end of the auditorium, and the area in front of the stage were destroyed. It was thought that a lighted cigarette-end had become wedged between a tip-up seat and its back, at the end of the performance.

The Central became the 'Abbeygate' in 1959, with Bury's

first ever film Cinemascope screen, and the distinction of hosting Bury's first ever film première the film in question was 'Please Turn Over', and amongst the stars who made personal appearances were Ted Ray, Jean Kent, Leslie Phillips and Joan Sims. The cinema dropped the name, 'Abbeygate', in 1971, and since then, it has had several changes of name. At the time of writing it is known as the Cannon. An alternative title might be the Survivor, since it is now the only remaining cinema in the town.

The Playhouse in the Buttermarket opened in 1925, when Jackie Coogan and Rin-Tin-Tin were winning the public's hearts. With its coloured glass awning and smart entrance it was highly regarded.

The Odeon in Brentgovel Street opened in 1937 when the film industry was at its peak. The Managing Director of the Odeon group of cinemas, Oscar Deutsch, a brilliant business-man, had in the space of four years established 221 cinemas throughout the country, all constructed to the highest stan-dards. Deutsch always publicised the fact that he used only British materials, manufactured by British workmen, during this period of national Depression, and he took a personal pride in each individual building in the chain. As far as the Bury Odeon was concerned, every contemporary refinement had been included in the design. On the walls were perforated tiles which eliminated reverberation or echo. The air was changed every three-and-a-half minutes, and kept at an even temperature. The screen, of a new metal, was one of the finest in the country. The audience of thirteen hundred who arrived for its opening passed through an entrance-hall fragrant with flowers, that had been sent up from Covent Garden. The Mayor performed the opening ceremony. Speeches were made. Then everyone settled down to enjoy two films, a cartoon, and the newsreel, (that bill-of-fare which every middle-aged British cinema-goer must remember with nostal-gia). In this case the feature-film was 'Beloved Enemy', starring Merle Oberon.

When I first met the former Odeon, it had changed its name to the Focus. I had a special affection for the Focus cinema. When we first moved to Bury, and my young daughter was pining for her old home, visits to the Focus cheered her up. And the building awakened memories of my own childhood. For it was similar in design to the smart, suburban picture-house in Glasgow, to which I was taken by my parents on Friday evenings to sigh over the beauty of Margaret Lockwood, or shrink from the scowling, saturnine face of James Mason.

In 1982 a redevelopment scheme for Brentgovel Street was approved. In October of that year the Focus showed its last film, (fittingly, the nostalgic evergreen, 'Snow White'.) Today, where a fine cinema once stood, is a piece of derelict land. That it will soon be covered with houses and shops is, I'm afraid no consolation to me. I still mourn my old friend.

THE BATTLE FOR THE ABBEY GARDENS PARK

'This,' my young visitor declared, with a child's clear-eyed assessment of the scene before him, 'is a park for absolutely everyone!'

We were standing in Bury's Abbey Gardens at the end of an idyllic Spring day, and watching the swans amble across the bowling green. Our circuit had necessarily been a slow one because of the number of diversions on our route. To begin with there had been the enchanting business of stepping out of the busy hum of Angel Hill, beneath the fearsome-looking portcullis of the shadow-filled Abbey Gateway, and into a world that was suddenly vibrant with colour. For the magnificent floral displays produced by the Park Superintendent and his staff are sufficiently breathcatching to stop even a lively nine-year-old in his tracks. Having veered to the left across what was once the Great Court of the Abbey, we found another source of wonder in the exotic plumage of the birds in the aviary. Then we had to watch the young men and their girls showing off a little on the putting green. After this there were the ducks to feed on the River Lark, the swings and roundabouts to be appraised and thoroughly tested, the tennis-players to inspect, the Abbey ruins to be viewed, and great open stretches to be raced across, until legs finally buckled and one happy small boy lay, prostrate and panting, on the grass. Yes, truly, this was a park for everyone. But as I looked down on my companion's radiant face, it struck me that I knew nothing of how this state of affairs had come about.

I had a feeling, that, hidden in the mists of the not-too-distant past, there was probably a public champion, (or champions) to whom I and my younger visitor ought to be heartfeltly grateful. My subsequent researches introduced me to the gentlemen in question.

From the beginning of the nineteenth century at least, part of the Abbey grounds had been laid out as Botanic Gardens, but these were open only to those wealthier members of the community who could pay the subscription for admission. In 1831 Nathaniel S. H. Hodgson, gentleman, of Bury, obtained from Lord Bristol a twenty-one years' lease for the six acres of the Abbey Gardens, including 'Abbeygate, stones etc. and trees, as a public Botanic Gardens' and for this he paid sixty pounds per annum. Then in 1892 Alfred Latimer Hooper of Bury obtained from Lord Bristol a three years' lease of the Botanic Gardens for which he paid over £166 per annum. It was in this same year that Alderman Frederick Andrews first mooted the idea of turning the Gardens into a public free park, but it was rejected both by the Council and by the ratepayers who were unwilling to pay the small extra rate this would entail. Finally in 1909 the small but dynamic body known as the Town Improvement Committee, (the same Committee which had organised the celebrated Bury Pageant of 1907) voiced the opinion that the Gardens ought to be made free of access to all, both because a town of Bury's size needed a public park and because they felt that the town ought to have responsibility for the Abbey ruins. When George the Fifth came to the throne the following year, it was suggested that the Gardens be opened to commemorate his coronation.

The altruistic councillors, however, with Alderman Owen Clark and Alderman Thomas Nice as their leaders, were to find the road ahead a stony one. To begin with, having had a valuation made, they found they would require not less than £650 to compensate the Marquis of Bristol for unexpired tenancy and other expenses. As the Council could not consider laying out such a large capital sum, Alderman Clark asked for fourteen days' grace in which to endeavour to raise the amount by subscription. The first generous donation of £200 came from Bury's M.P., the Honourable Walter Guinness, with a promise of further financial help, if it were needed. Other prominent figures in the locality following suit, the required £650 was soon gathered.

Even with the initial obstacle overcome, terms for the transfer of the Gardens could still not be agreed upon. There was soon a stalemate in the negotiations, and even the scheme's most ardent supporters began to lose heart and to consider abandoning the project. But not so the indomitable Alderman Clark, who went up to London on behalf of his Committee, met the solicitors of the Marquis of Bristol and succeeded, (by sheer force of personality, so Alderman Nice maintained) in bringing the deal to a satisfactory conclusion.

The Botanic Garden c. 1850. The Botanic Garden was established in 1820 by N. S. Hodson, Esq., who filled it initially with his private collection of plants. He was still Superintendent there in 1844 according to the local *Directories*, and the Garden was much patronised by the nobility, gentry, and principal inhabitants of the town and neighbourhood

The Abbey Gardens were officially opened as a free park on Saturday, December 28, 1912. Not surprisingly, in view of the time of year, the weather was unsympathetic. As the crowds gathered on Angel Hill, so apparently did the clouds in the heavens and it was in heavily-falling rain that the civic procession made its damp and stately way from the Guildhall, down Abbeygate Street and across Angel Hill to the Abbey Gateway. The entrance to the latter was roped off and guarded by policemen and by the newly appointed Park Keeper. Lady Evelyn Guinness, who was to declare the park open, arrived with her husband just after three o'clock. Happily the rain eased off while the ceremony was performed and the gates unlocked. The official party then moved through to be photographed standing on a temporary platform that had been erected just inside the Gardens. Their faces look out at us still from the pages of the 'Bury Free Press', an incongruously funereal-looking group considering the occasion. Sombre, bearded gentlemen in top hats standing in the rain with the portcullis of the Abbey Gateway threatening to snap its teeth in the background. Only Lady Evelyn in her pretty floral hat has managed a brave little smile.

There were to be speeches made from the platform by Alderman Nice and Alderman Clarke, telling the history behind the park's purchase and with more than one admonition to its future public about their behaviour therein. Alas. The heavens opened before even the preliminaries were completed and the speakers with the rest of the party were forced to bolt into the Abbey Gateway. The speeches, inaudible to what must surely have been a rapidly dispersing audience, were nevertheless dutifully reported by the Press. A telegram was sent to Sandringham to inform the King that Bury had opened its first public park to commemorate his coronation, to which despatch a congratulatory reply was later received. And, at the end of the day, as so many others have done before and since, they all adjourned to the 'Angel' for a warming cup of tea and some sustenance. I hope they were happy. They certainly deserved to be. For as Alderman Clarke had pointed out in his speech 'to be truly happy we must communicate happiness to others'. And he and his colleagues had most certainly fulfilled the conditions of that particular contract!

BOMBARDMENT

We sometimes tend to forget that the First World War was not fought exclusively on foreign battlefields. Even a country-town like Bury St Edmunds could become, as it did on two occasions, the target for enemy bombing. It is difficult to imagine those scenes just over seventy years ago, when the dreaded German airships hung in the sky over the town. It must have been a terrifying experience. Yet, according to press reports of both bombings, the local population reacted with admirable courage and level-headedness.

The first raid took place on April 30, 1915. A police constable called Wright was on duty in Southgate Street at around 12.35 a.m. when he heard what he thought were tiles sliding from a roof. We can only imagine his feelings, when he looked up and saw what he described as the 'shining, cigar-shaped body of the Zeppelin.' He didn't have long to ponder, though, for, as he watched, bombs trailing a bluish light began to whistle down about forty yards away. As the third bomb dropped the whole district was lit up and the constable blew his whistle to warn the residents. The owner of a local bakehouse, who had also seen the Zeppelin, reacted with laudable promptitude by throwing pails of water on to the bombs.

Mr Hinnels of Churchgate Street heard the noise, too. He thought it was caused by trains at the station, until he looked out and saw what he described as 'a pencil' sailing gracefully across the sky. The airship shed four more bombs in the St Andrews Street area. One just behind the Castle, one on Boby's works, one in the Pits near the hospital and the last, further out, just beyond the Ouida Memorial.

To Mr Thompson of Cemetery Road, now King's Road, the buzzing noises sounded like the engines of the Electricity Lighting Station. But a loud bang, apparently outside his back door, and a blinding flash of light in his bedroom, sent him rushing out to his yard at the very moment that the Zeppelin came over his house. He dived for his cellar as the airship dropped three of its bombs before turning away again to the south.

Another eye-witness in the Buttermarket was also blaming the Electricity Works for the noise. Then he heard explosions and saw smoke begin to rise from the very heart of the town. Mr Gamble, the chemist in Abbeygate Street, however, attributed the curious noise to a motor-engine, left idling

A 1915 incendiary bomb. These iron bombs did plenty of damage, but in fact were of a fairly simple design. Just over a foot long, their core was a perforated brass tube filled with an incendiary mixture. The bombs were weighted with lead at the bottom and had an unsophisticated priming device at the top.

somewhere near his shop. What seems clear is that very few residents of the town had been expecting a nocturnal visit from a Zep.

Fortunately, and amazingly, on this occasion there was damage only to property. No-one was killed or even injured. The estimate of bombs dropped varied from between twenty-five to fifty, all but four of these being incendiary devices. The shops destroyed, or badly damaged, in the Buttermarket were Day's, the shoemaker's, which was gutted. Mrs Wise's. T. H. Nice's, the motor and cycle agents'. Messrs Johnsons', the dyers and Miss Clark's, the tobacconists. During the following week-end visitors thronged into the town to inspect the scenes of devastation.

The newspaper headlines after the 1915 raid were 'Aerial Visitation of the Baby Killers!' This seems, in retrospect, tragically prophetic when we read the reports of Bury's second Zeppelin bombardment, which took place on the night of March 31 – April 1, 1916. For on this occasion lives were lost. Among the victims were a mother and her two babies.

By 1916, censorship had tightened to such an extent that newspapers were not allowed to give precise locations in their reports of bombing-raids, not even the name of the town or city concerned. The 'Bury Free Press' could only report that 'A certain ancient and well-known town received the attention of Zeppelins twice during Friday night'. From accounts of the raid that were published, though, we know that it was the south and west ends of the town that were bombed on this occasion, although there were only seven fatalities in the raid, the misery and suffering inflicted on the victims and their families had the whole town grieving.

Again because of censorship regulations, the names of the dead were not given, but the identities of six of them can be ascertained from the subsequent acknowledgements and 'In Memoriam' notices in the local paper.

182

The mother, who died so tragically with her two babies, was a Mrs Durball, aged thirty-four, an Irish woman, and the wife of a drummer in the 3rd Suffolk Regiment. A bomb scored a direct hit on their cottage, falling into the bedroom and carrying the bed through to the room beneath. A third child had its feet blown off in the explosion.

Another heavy loss was sustained by the Adams family of Raingate Street. Sixty-year-old Mr Henry Adams, a Corporation official, had some horses in his care, and when the raid started, he hurried out with three of his sons to see that the animals were all right. A bomb fell directly in their path, killing outright both Mr Adams and his fifteen year old son, George.

Hubert Hardiment, a youth of twenty, was lodging in one of the cottages that was bombed. At his landlady's request, he had run downstairs to the back door to find out what was happening. A bomb fell into the back garden and blew the rear of the cottage to pieces killing him instantly.

The seventh victim was buried in the ruins of his house and although his six-year-old son immediately summoned the

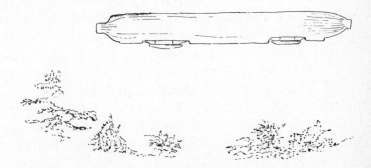

A Zeppelin bearing against the wind. 'Men raise themselves no longer merely as play-balls, subject to the wind's caprices, but themselves choosing their paths of travel to their destinations. It was when this was first accomplished that the command of God was realised, that all creation should be subject to man.' Count Zeppelin. 1909.

assistance of a neighbouring stonemason to dig him out, the poor man died from his injuries the following day.

Once again the disaster brought sightseers flocking to the town in their hundreds. One enterprising neighbour stood outside the ruins with a collecting dish, receiving donations for the families of the bereaved. This, it seems, was typical of Bury's reaction to the death that had suddenly rained down on them. They mourned for the victims, but shock and grief and outrage had not robbed them of their practical common sense.

INDEX

Abbey, 19, 20, *21*, 29, 81, 127
Abbey Gardens, 78, 175
Abbey Gate, 21, 81, 82, *127*, 175
Abbeygate Street, 35–38, 46–48,
    56, 80, 121–124, 128, 169, 178,
    181
Abbot's Bridge, 82, 162
Anderson's Coffee House, 72
Angel Hill, 22–24, 28, 32, 35, 65,
    69, 81, 82, 103, 122, 124, 127,
    128, 175, 178
Angel Hotel, 22, 30, 83, 103, 125,
    128
Angel Lane, 29
Assembly Rooms, 84, 87, 88, 122,
    125
Athenaeum, 22, 156

Bates, Ronald, 169
Bloomfield, Robert, 121
Botanic Gardens, *127*, 160, *162*,
    176, *177*
Brentgovel Street, 173, 174
Bridewell Lane, 29, 32
Buck, William, 97, 98
Bury, Samuel, 55–58
Bury Free Library, 144
Bury Racecourse, 158
Bury Record Office, 52, 56, 60,
    121, 144, 164, 170
Bury St Edmunds Art Gallery,
    59, 63, 153
Buttermarket, 35, 46, 126, 143
Butts, 163

Cattle Market, 25

Central Cinema, 172
Chalk Lane, 32, 50
Charles II, 21
Chequer Square, 102, 103, 106
Churchgate Street, 29, 54, 55, 56,
    180
Clarke, Owen, 120, 146, 176–178
Clarkson, Catherine, 95–97
Clarkson, Thomas, 95–97
Coke, Arundel, 65–68, 82
College Square, 32
Cook's Row, 56, 80
Corn Exchange, 140, 142
Cornhill, 39, 47, 48, 80, 140, 172
Crispe, Edward, 65–68, 82
Culford Hall, 21
Cullum, Milner-Gibson, Mr, 144,
    146

Defoe, Daniel, 24, 56
Donne, W. B., 110, 153
Duke of York's Own Loyal
    Suffolk Hussars, 21

Eastgate Street, 34, 163
Edmund, Saint, 20
Edward VII, 20, *22*
Edward the Confessor, 19
Elmswell, 20

Fitzgerald, Edward, 107–112
Focus Cinema, *171*, 174
Foote, Samuel, 61
Fornham Road, 21
Fox, George, 41

187

ABOUT THE AUTHOR

Elsie McCutcheon was born and educated in Glasgow. She taught English there before moving to East Anglia with her husband in 1964. While living in Norfolk she became interested in archaeology, and worked for several years on an amateur 'dig' near Lowestoft, as well as being Publicity Officer for Norfolk Archaeology Rescue Group. In 1975 she extended her interest to documents and became a frequenter of Record Offices. She currently edits the newsletter of the Friends of the Suffolk Record Office. Her published works include five children's novels, (all set in Suffolk), and hundreds of articles and short stories, written for a wide range of magazines and newspapers over a period of twenty years. She lives in the village of Horringer near Bury St Edmunds.

Other books by Elsie McCutcheon

The Moonlight Paupers

Summer of the Zeppelin
Runner-up for the Guardian Award 1983

The Rat War

Smokescreen

Storm Bird